# Telecourse Study Guide for

# *Against All Odds: Inside Statistics* and *Introduction to the Practice of Statistics*

SECOND EDITION

# Telecourse Study Guide for

# *Against All Odds: Inside Statistics* and *Introduction to the Practice of Statistics*

SECOND EDITION

David S. Moore
*Purdue University*

**W. H. Freeman and Company**
New York

*Cover illustration by Salem Krieger*

Major funding for the *Against All Odds: Inside Statistics* telecourse and for the television series has been provided by the Annenberg/CBP Project.



Printed in the United States of America.

ISBN 0-7167-2452-9

Fifth printing 1995, RRD

# CONTENTS

# INTRODUCTION

*Against All Odds: Inside Statistics* is a series of 26 half-hour television shows that introduces modern statistical methods in the context of a wide variety of real-world applications. The power of television comes largely from its ability to take you out of the classroom to visit users of statistics: quality engineers, medical researchers, government bureaus, environmentalists, potato chip makers, and many others. But television alone is an inadequate vehicle for learning. It does not allow explanation of details or carefully-worked examples, and does not provide exercises to build understanding through doing. A text provides these essential features.

The purpose of this study guide is to guide your learning of basic statistics by linking the television programs in *Against All Odds: Inside Statistics* with the telecourse text:

> David S. Moore and George P. McCabe
> *Introduction to the Practice of Statistics*
> W. H. Freeman and Company, Second Edition, 1992

The study guide breaks the course material into units, each of which corresponds to one of the television programs. For each unit, we state specific learning objectives and give a reading assignment in the text.

Each unit also contains a problem assignment and self-test questions with fully worked solutions.

## HOW TO USE THIS STUDY GUIDE

Learning comes about mainly by your own efforts. Television programs and a written text present the material to you in different ways, but you must work actively in order to learn. This is particularly true in learning a subject like statistics, where one of your goals is to be able to actually carry out statistical work. You must learn by doing. The problem assignments are the center of learning by doing. Your purpose in working a problem is not to get the answer in the back of the book as quickly as possible, but to be sure that in similar situations you will be able to recognize what statistical skills are needed and to carry out the work accurately. Do the assignments carefully, returning to the text or asking for help until you not only have the correct answer but are confident that you can do other similar problems efficiently.

Statistics requires much calculating and graphing. You will need lots of *graph paper*. You must also have a *calculator*. A scientific calculator that will compute means and standard deviations is well worth the few extra dollars. Some calculators have many other statistical features, such as fitting least squares regression lines.

> **Hint**: Most mistakes in using a calculator that has statistical functions are due to entering the data incorrectly. It is a good idea to do your calculations twice, including entering the data a second time.

In practice, statistical work is often done by computer software. If you have access to a computer system that will do statistical calculations and graphs, we encourage you to use it. But because many telecourse students do not use computers, the problems assigned are chosen so that the calculations are manageable with only a calculator.

## HOW TO MASTER A UNIT IN THIS STUDY GUIDE

1. Watch the *television program* for the unit. The program will introduce the important concepts of the unit, and will illustrate their application in several settings. Remember that you will not be tested on details of the examples used to illustrate the statistical ideas, only on the statistics itself. After watching the television program you should have an overall grasp of the content of the unit, but you may not be confident that you can work problems about the content. The text and this study guide will help you learn the necessary detail.

2. Read the *learning objectives* for the unit, which are given at the beginning of each unit in this study guide. These objectives tell you exactly what you must learn in order to master the unit. They will help you know what to look for in the reading.

3. Read the assigned portion of the *text*. The reading will usually give more detail than the television. Pay particular attention to specific skills such as numerical calculations. There is not time to go through most calculations carefully in the television program, so you must learn the steps from the text.

4. Do the *assigned problems* from the text. In most cases, you can check your answers against those given in the back of the book. If you have difficulty with the assignment, you should seek help. Your institution

will have an arrangement to provide assistance when you need it. It may also be helpful to watch the television program again.

5. Finally, try the *self-test questions* for the unit. Some of the self-test questions are taken from the text, but complete solutions are given in this study guide so that you can check your work in detail. If you can do the self-test questions, you can be confident that you have mastered the important material of the unit. Resist the temptation to look at the solutions before you have made a serious attempt to solve the problems yourself. Try to do all of the self-test questions before looking at any of the solutions. This will give you an honest assessment of how well you know the material. The solutions in the study guide will then fill minor gaps in your knowledge.

## OUTLINE OF THE TELECOURSE

Each unit in this study guide corresponds to a television program in *Against All Odds.* Three of the 26 programs differ from the others and are not accompanied by the usual learning objectives and problem assignment. The first program is an introduction and overview. Program 10 shows some modern uses of computer graphics in statistics and reviews the first segment of the course by means of a case study. Program 26 is a concluding case study that reviews the main ideas of the course. The study guide units for the remaining 23 programs are similar in kind.

**Program 1 What is Statistics?** An overview of the nature and impact of statistics based on short views of applications that appear later in the series. This program also introduces the series host, Professor Teresa Amabile, and her research on creativity in children.

**Program 2 Picturing Distributions** Presenting and interpreting the distribution of a single variable. Techniques taught include stemplots, frequency tables and histograms. Stories: patterns in lightning strikes and in the demographics of television viewers.

**Program 3 Numerical Description of Distributions** Numerical measures of specific aspects of a distribution: center (mean, median), spread (percentiles, the five-number summary, boxplots, and the standard deviation). Resistance and its lack. Stories: Comparing the pay of men and women; calories in hot dogs; setting urine tests to music.

**Program 4 Normal Distributions** Topics: Density curves as smoothed histograms; mean, median, percentiles for density curves; the normal distributions (general shape, locating $\mu$ and $\sigma$, the 68–95–99.7 rule). Stories: A social club for tall people, baseball's .400 hitters.

**Program 5 Normal Calculations** Standardizing observations and calculating normal relative frequencies from tables; assessing normality by normal quantile plots. Stories: Nitrogen oxide levels in auto exhausts, measuring blood cholesterol, the sizes of the Army's soldiers.

**Program 6 Time Series** From the distribution of a single variable we move to an examination of change over time. Topics: Statistical control, inspecting time series for trend, seasonal variation, cycles; smoothing by averaging, either over many units per time or over time by running medians. Stories: Our biological clocks, electrical signals in the brain, cycles in stock market prices.

**Program 7 Models For Growth** Mathematical models for the overall pattern of simple kinds of growth over time. Topics: Linear growth, with review of the geometry of straight lines and an introduction to the least-squares idea; exponential growth and straightening an exponential growth curve by logarithms; prediction and extrapolation. Stories: growth hormone deficiency, gypsy moth outbreaks.

**Program 8 Describing Relationships** Topics: Scatterplots and their variations, smoothing scatterplots of response vs. explanatory variable by median trace; linear relationships, least-squares regression lines, outliers and influential observations. Stories: The fate of Florida manatees, the draft lottery, why dieting fails.

**Program 9 Correlation** Correlation and its properties; the relation between correlation and regression. Stories: study of heredity versus environment in twins, the lively ball in baseball, the Coleman Report on effects of schooling.

**Program 10 Multidimensional Data Analysis** The impact of computing technology on statistics, especially graphics for displaying multidimensional data. A case study in data analysis: environmental monitoring of Chesapeake Bay.

**Program 11 The Question of Causation** Association between categorical variables displayed in a two-way table; Simpson's paradox; the varied relations among variables that can underlie an observed association; how evidence for causation is obtained. Story: Smoking and health.

**Program 12 Experimental Design** Advantages of planned data collection over anecdotal evidence or available data; observation versus experiment. Basic principles of experimental design: comparison, and randomization. Use of a table of random digits. Stories: The behavior of lobsters, a medical experiment on aspirin and heart attacks, an experiment on police response to domestic violence.

**Program 13 Experiments and Samples** Further principles of design: two or more factors and blocking. Introduction to sample surveys: the danger of bias, random sampling. Stories: An agricultural experiment on strawberries, the U.S. Census, sampling in the making of potato chips.

**Program 14 Sampling and Sampling Distributions** More elaborate sample designs: stratified and multistage designs. The practical difficulties of sampling human populations. The idea of a sampling distribution. Stories: A survey of recreational fishing, the General Social Survey.

**Program 15 What is Probability?** Probability as a model for long term relative frequencies or personal assessment of chance. Sample space, basic rules of assigning probability: $0 \leq P(A) \leq 1$, $P(S) = 1$, addition rule for disjoint events. Stories: Persi Diaconis discusses randomness, studying the flow of traffic.

**Program 16 Random Variables** Independence and the multiplication rule for independent events. Discrete and continuous random variables. Mean and variance of a random variable. Stories: The movie *Stand and Deliver*, the space shuttle *Challenger* disaster, predicting earthquakes.

**Program 17 Binomial Distributions** The law of large numbers. Addition rules for means and variances of random variables. The binomial distributions for sample counts. Normal approximation to binomial distributions. Stories: The hot hand in basketball, returns on risky investments, sickle cell anemia.

**Program 18 The Sample Mean and Control Charts** The sampling distribution of $\overline{x}$. The central limit theorem. $\overline{x}$ control charts and statistical process control. Stories: gambling casinos, quality control in making potato chips.

**Program 19 Confidence Intervals** The reasoning behind confidence intervals; $z$-intervals for the mean of a normal distribution. Behavior of confidence intervals. Stories: Opinion polls, estimating the lifetimes of batteries, using primates in research.

**Program 20 Significance Tests** The reasoning behind significance tests illustrated by the case of tests about a normal mean with known standard deviation. Null and alternative hypotheses and $P$-values, and cautions on the limited information provided by tests. Stories: Did Shakespeare write a newly-discovered poem? Did the FBI discriminate against its Hispanic agents?

**Program 21 Inference for One Mean** Inference about the mean of a single distribution, with emphasis on paired samples as the most important practical use of these procedures. The one-sample $t$ confidence interval and test. Stories: The National Institute of Standards and Technology, taste testing of a new cola, assessing autistic children.

**Program 22 Comparing Two Means** Recognizing two-sample problems. The two-sample $t$ confidence intervals and tests for comparing means; brief mention of the sensitivity of the corresponding procedures for variances to nonnormality and their consequent impracticality. Stories: Assessing welfare reform, testing a new type of foam seating, the effect of coaching on SAT scores.

**Program 23 Inference for Proportions** Confidence intervals and tests for a single proportion and for comparing proportions based two independent samples. Stories: The Bureau of Labor Statistics and the unemployment rate, contaminated water and cancer in Woburn, Massachusetts, the Salem witch trials.

**Program 24 Inference for Two-Way Tables** Displaying data in a two-way table. The chi-square test for independence/equal distributions in two-way tables. Stories: Studying fossil teeth, comparing the treatment of breast cancer in younger and older women, did Gregor Mendel fudge his data?

**Program 25 Inference for Relationships** Inference for simple linear regression, emphasizing the slope and prediction of mean response and individual response. Stories: Estimating the Hubble constant for the expanding universe, predicting the birth date of a baby from ultrasound data.

**Program 26 Case Study** The development and testing of the drug AZT, the first effective treatment for AIDS, with emphasis on the role of statistical studies.

# UNIT 1
# WHAT IS STATISTICS?

## LESSON OVERVIEW

Statistics deals with **data**, or numerical facts. In this course you will first learn methods for organizing and describing data (Units 1 to 10). Units 11 to 14 concern the production of data to answer specific questions. The remaining units present methods of statistical inference, that is, methods for drawing conclusions from data. Because formal inference uses probability to state how reliable our conclusions are, Units 15 to 18 present the probability that is needed to understand inference. Units 19 to 25 discuss inference itself, and Unit 26 is a concluding case study. The video will help acquaint you with the nature of statistics and its varied applications. Later programs will show many specific uses of statistics in more detail.

## ASSIGNMENT

1. Be certain that you are familiar with the operation of this telecourse. You should know when the video programs will be shown,

when assignments are due and how to turn them in, and when and where examinations will be given. You should also know how to get additional help if you need it and how your grade will be established.

2. Read the Prefaces and the introductory section "What is Statistics" in the text.

3. There is no written assignment for this introductory unit.

## LEARNING OBJECTIVES

A. Know that statistics has three goals: organizing and describing data, producing new data, and drawing conclusions from data (inference).

B. Recognize the usefulness of statistics by observing how common data are in academic study, in many occupations, and in everyday life.

# UNIT 2
# PICTURING DISTRIBUTIONS

## LESSON OVERVIEW

A **variable** is any numerical characteristic of a person, animal, or thing. The values of a variable vary when measurements are made on different people or things, or at different times. The **distribution** of a variable describes its pattern of variation by giving the values of the variable and how often the values occur. This unit shows how graphs can be used to help us see the major features of the distribution of a single variable.

You should look first for the **overall pattern** of the distribution, and then for major **deviations** from that pattern. The shape of the distribution—**symmetric** or **skewed**—is an important aspect of the overall pattern. The **center** and **spread** of the distribution are also important. Deviations from the pattern may take the form of **outliers** or of gaps and other irregularities in the distribution. Distributions can be pictured by **stemplots** of the values or by **histograms** when the values are grouped into classes.

The video begins with the search for a pattern in lightning strikes. A histogram of lightning flashes in Colorado shows that the distribution of the hour of the first flash in a day is surprisingly regular. It is quite symmetric and centered near noon. A histogram of the hour with the maximum number of flashes is centered in the late afternoon, with a few outliers in the early morning. These distributions suggest explanations for lightning storms based on local wind patterns. When you make a histogram, you must first group your observations into classes. The video shows graphically how either too many or too few classes produce an uninformative histogram.

Often we want to compare several distributions. You watch the program director of a television station compare the age distributions for the viewers of two programs in the process of deciding which program to air. These distributions are skewed. Then you see a comparison of the number of hysterectomies performed by male and female gynecologists. This example shows how stemplots completely display the distribution of a small number of observations, and how **back-to-back stemplots** show comparisons clearly.

**Plots against time**, which are also important in understanding the behavior of a variable, receive more extended treatment in Unit 6.

## ASSIGNMENT

1. Read the LEARNING OBJECTIVES to see what specific skills you must acquire from this unit.

2. Read Section 1.1 of the text. The concluding section on time plots is optional now; you will study this topic in Unit 6.

3. Do the following problems from the SECTION 1.1 EXERCISES in

the text: 1.1, 1.13, 1.19(a), 1.26, 1.28.

4. Finally, try the SELF-TEST QUESTIONS and compare your answers with those given.

## LEARNING OBJECTIVES

### A. STEMPLOTS

1. Make a stemplot of a the distribution of a small number of observations (say $n \leq 50$).
2. Truncate leaves or split stems when needed to make an effective stemplot.
3. Make a back-to-back stemplot with common stems to compare two similar distributions.

### B. HISTOGRAMS

1. Make a histogram when you are given a frequency table with classes of equal widths.
2. Make a histogram of the distribution of a moderate number of observations (say $n \leq 200$) by choosing classes of equal widths, preparing a frequency table, and drawing the histogram.

C. DISTRIBUTIONS

1. Learn to inquire exactly what is measured and how when first inspecting a set of data.

2. Calculate the frequency (count) and relative frequency (proportion or percent) of any value in a data set.

3. Learn when inspecting a distribution to look first for the overall pattern and then for major deviations from the pattern.

4. Assess from a stemplot or histogram whether a distribution is roughly symmetric or distinctly skewed and whether it has one peak or several.

5. Assess where a distribution is centered by finding the median (half of the observations are greater and half less), and compare the spreads of several similar distributions.

6. Recognize outliers.

## SELF-TEST QUESTIONS

**2.1** In 1988 there were 1,436 two-year colleges in the United States, of which 984 were public institutions. What is the relative frequency of public two-year colleges?

**2.2** Here is a frequency table for the hour at which the first flash of lightning each day was observed in a study in Colorado. (Hour 1 stands for midnight to 1 am, and so on.)

| Hour | Count | Hour | Count | Hour | Count |
|---|---|---|---|---|---|
| 1 | 0 | 9 | 3 | 17 | 2 |
| 2 | 0 | 10 | 5 | 18 | 0 |
| 3 | 0 | 11 | 16 | 19 | 0 |
| 4 | 0 | 12 | 23 | 20 | 0 |
| 5 | 0 | 13 | 11 | 21 | 0 |
| 6 | 0 | 14 | 3 | 22 | 0 |
| 7 | 2 | 15 | 4 | 23 | 0 |
| 8 | 1 | 16 | 1 | 24 | 0 |

(a) Make a histogram of these data.
(b) Describe the distribution: Is it roughly symmetric or distinctly skewed? Where is the center? At what time of day does the first flash most often occur? Are there any outliers?

**2.3** Here is a table of the number of hysterectomies performed by each of a group of Swiss doctors. The data are recorded separately for male and female doctors.

| Male | | | | | Female | | | | |
|---|---|---|---|---|---|---|---|---|---|
| 27 | 59 | 33 | 25 | 86 | 5 | 31 | 29 | 14 | 18 |
| 25 | 85 | 31 | 37 | 44 | 10 | 7 | 25 | 33 | 0 |
| 20 | 36 | 50 | 34 | 28 | 18 | | | | |

(a) Make a stemplot of the entire data set. Describe the distribution: Is it symmetric or skewed? Where is the median (half the doctors perform more hysterectomies than this and half perform less)? Are there outliers?
(b) Make a back-to-back stemplot to compare male and female doctors. What is the most obvious difference between the two distributions?

**2.4** A survey of the hourly wages earned by students working part-time during the school year produces data such as \$4.35, \$5.50, \$7.10, and \$ 4.85. Show how you would truncate data such as these to make a stemplot by writing the stems and leaves for these four observations on a small stemplot.

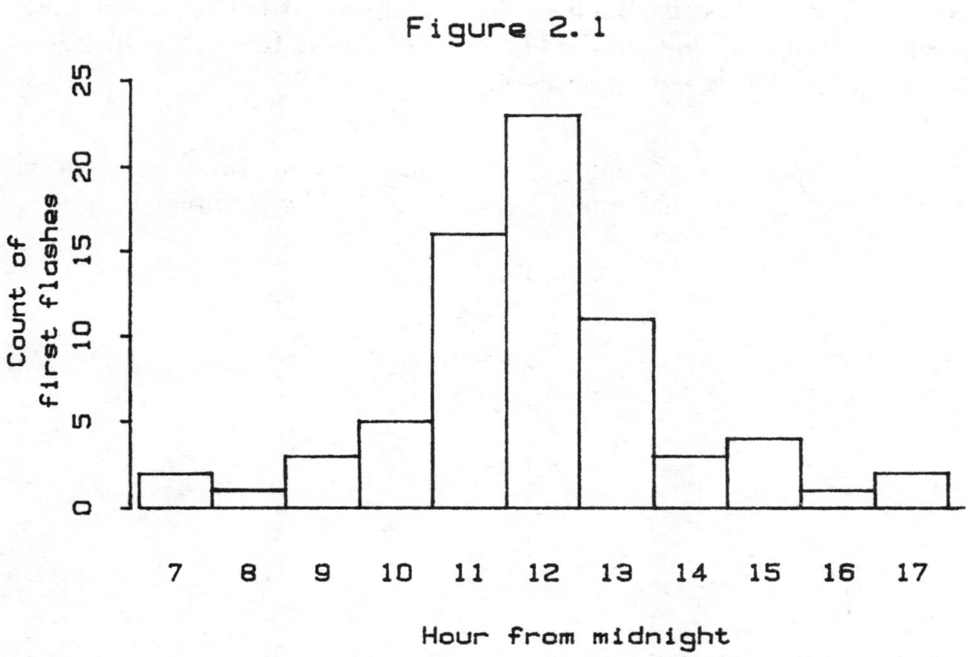


## SELF-TEST SOLUTIONS

**2.1** Relative frequency is just the fraction, proportion, or percent of public colleges among all two-year colleges. The relative frequency is

$$\frac{984}{1436} = .685 = 68.5\%$$

The answer is usually given as a percent.

**2.2** (a) The histogram drawn from this frequency table appears in Figure 2.1.
(b) The distribution is roughly symmetric. It is centered in Hour 12 (on 27 days the first flash fell earlier, on 21 days it fell later, and on 23 days it fell during this hour). The peak is also at Hour 12, which is 11 am to noon. There are no outliers.

**2.3** (a) To make the stemplot of all 26 observations, take the first digit to be the stem and the second to be the leaf. The stemplot is

| Stem | Leaves |
|---|---|
| 0 | 057 |
| 1 | 0488 |
| 2 | 0555789 |
| 3 | 1133467 |
| 4 | 4 |
| 5 | 09 |
| 6 | |
| 7 | |
| 8 | 56 |

There are two apparent outliers, 85 and 86, in the high tail. The distribution is skewed to the right if these two extreme values are included, but the skewness is rather small if we ignore the outliers. This points out again that in many cases symmetry/skewness is a judgment call. By counting up 13 (half of 26) observations, we find the median at 28 or 29 depending on which end we count from. This locates the center accurately enough for now. The next unit will give an exact recipe for finding the median.
(b) Here is the required back-to-back stemplot. Male doctors are on the left and female doctors on the right. Remember that the final step

is to arrange the leaves in increasing order *away from the stem.*

| | | |
|---:|:---:|:---|
| | 0 | 057 |
| | 1 | 0488 |
| 87550 | 2 | 59 |
| 76431 | 3 | 13 |
| 4 | 4 | |
| 90 | 5 | |
| | 6 | |
| | 7 | |
| 65 | 8 | |

The most obvious difference between the two distributions is that male doctors as a group perform many more hysterectomies than do female doctors. The centers are about 34 for males and 18 for females. Five of the 15 males performed more hysterectomies than any of the females.

**2.4** Take dollars as the stems, then truncate by discarding the last (pennies) digit in each number. Notice that truncating is different from rounding the numbers. Truncation is used in stemplots because it is faster. The result is:

| | |
|---:|:---|
| 4 | 38 |
| 5 | 5 |
| 6 | |
| 7 | 1 |

# UNIT 3
# DESCRIBING DISTRIBUTIONS

## LESSON OVERVIEW

This unit shows how numerical measures can give compact descriptions of specific aspects of a distribution. The **median** and the **mean** are measures of the center or location of a distribution. The mean is the average of the observations and the median is their midpoint. You will learn how these measures differ, in particular that the median is more **resistant** than the mean to the influence of extreme observations. The **quartiles**, which mark the points 25% and 75% up the ordered list of observations, are used with the median to measure spread. If the distribution is symmetric, the **interquartile range** (distance between the quartiles) is a single number that measures spread. The **five-number summary** gives a fuller description of a distribution; it consists of the median, the two quartiles, and the two extremes (smallest and largest values). The five-number summary leads to a new graphical display for distributions, the **boxplot**. Finally, you will learn that when the mean measures center, spread is usually measured by the **standard deviation**.

The video begins with an examination of some differences between the distributions of incomes for male and female workers in the United States. These distributions are strongly skewed. The medians show the incomes of typical male and female workers, providing a numerical comparison. The explanation of the income gap between men and women is controversial.

A comparison of the number of calories in different brands of beef, meat, and poultry hot dogs illustrates the use of five-number summaries and boxplots to compare distributions. The data for this example appear in Table 1.4 of the text. Then the video looks at how researchers are using musical tones to help scan the results of medical urine tests—an off-key note alerts the technician that a value falls outside the normal range. The normal range is determined by using the standard deviation to measure the spread about the mean as center.

## ASSIGNMENT

1. Read the LEARNING OBJECTIVES to see what specific skills you must acquire from this unit.

2. Read Section 1.2 of the text.

3. Do the following problems from the SECTION 1.2 EXERCISES in the text: 1.41, 1.42, 1.44, 1.49, 1.59.

4. Finally, try the SELF-TEST QUESTIONS and compare your answers with those given.

# LEARNING OBJECTIVES

## A. MEASURING CENTER

1. Calculate the mean $\overline{x}$ of a set of observations, using a calculator.
2. Calculate the median $M$ of a small data set (say $n \leq 100$).
3. Understand that the median is more resistant than the mean; recognize when skewness in a distribution moves the mean away from the median toward the long tail.

## B. MEASURING SPREAD

1. Compute the quartiles $Q_1$ and $Q_3$ for a small data set.
2. Compute the inter-quartile range $IQR$ and use the $1.5 \times IQR$ criterion to identify outliers.
3. Give the five number summary and draw a boxplot or a modified boxplot; assess symmetry and skewness from a boxplot.
4. Compute the standard deviation $s$ for a small data set (say $n \leq 25$), using a calculator.
5. Know the basic properties of $s$: $s \geq 0$ always; $s = 0$ only when all observations are identical and increases as the spread increases; $s$ has the same units as the original measurements.
6. Decide which measure of spread is more appropriate: the standard deviation for symmetric distributions and when the mean is used to measure center, or the quartiles or five-number summary in skewed distributions and whenever the median is used to measure center.

## SELF-TEST QUESTIONS

**3.1** Anthropologists use the distribution of skull measurements to help classify ancient human remains. Here are measurements (in mm) on the forehead breadth of 12 skulls of the same type.

122 124 127 121 121 113 130 131 117 128 111 115

Calculate the mean and the standard deviation of this distribution.

**3.2** Problem 2.3 in the Unit 2 Self-Test reports the number of hysterectomies performed by each of 26 Swiss doctors.
(a) Find the five-number summary of this distribution (ignore the distinction between male and female doctors).
(b) Are the two extreme observations classed as outliers by the $1.5 \times IQR$ criterion?
(c) Call the Swiss doctors Group 1. The distribution of the numbers of hysterectomies performed by another group of doctors (Group 2) has five-number summary

1 10 17 30 51

and has no outliers by the $1.5 \times IQR$ criterion. Make modified side-by-side boxplots to compare the two groups. If you ignore any outliers, which distribution appears to be more strongly skewed?

**3.3** Answer the following questions:
(a) The distribution of income in a large group is usually strongly skewed to the right. The median household income in the U.S. was $29,943 in 1990. Was the mean family income larger or smaller? Why?
(b) A report on the distribution of fill weights for cola bottles says that, "The variation was very small; in fact, the standard deviation of

weight for the 25 bottles we weighed was only $s = -0.12$ grams." What is wrong with this statement?

## SELF-TEST SOLUTIONS

**3.1** Use a scientific calculator if possible. The computing formula is fastest if you must use a basic calculator. First compute

$$\begin{aligned} \sum x &= 1460 \\ \sum x^2 &= 178,120 \end{aligned}$$

Then

$$\begin{aligned} \overline{x} &= \frac{1460}{12} = 121.67 \\ s^2 &= \frac{1}{11}\{178,120 - \frac{1}{12}(1460)^2\} \\ &= \frac{1}{11}\{178,120 - 177,633.33\} = 44.24 \\ s &= \sqrt{44.24} = 6.65 \end{aligned}$$

**3.2** (a) First arrange the data in increasing order. It is easiest to simply use the stemplot that appears in the Unit 2 Self-Test solutions. Because $n = 26$, the median is located at the

$$\frac{n+1}{2} = \frac{27}{2} = 13.5$$

position, or halfway between the 13th and 14th observations in order. These observations are 28 and 29, so the median is $M = 28.5$. The first quartile is the median of the 13 observations below 28.5 and the third quartile is the median of the 13 observations that are greater than 28.5. That is, each quartile is the 7th in its group. So $Q_1 = 18$ and $Q_3 = 36$. The five-number summary is

$$0 \quad 18 \quad 28.5 \quad 36 \quad 86$$

(b) The inter-quartile range is

$$IQR = Q_3 - Q_1 = 36 - 18 = 18$$

so that $1.5 \times IQR = 27$. The extreme observations 85 and 86 are both more than 27 greater than the third quartile $Q_3 = 36$, so are marked as suspected outliers.

Figure 3.1

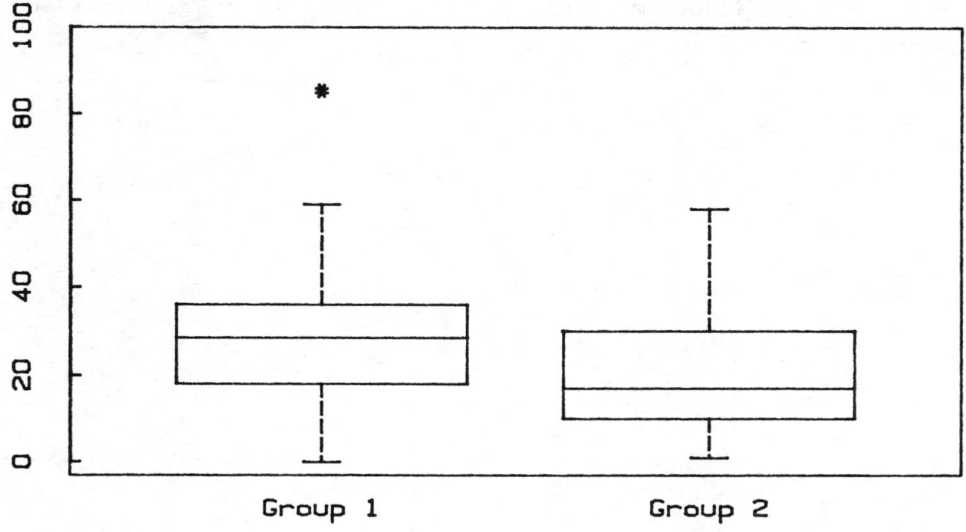

(c) The modified boxplots appear in Figure 3.1. In a modified boxplot, the outliers are plotted individually. This is the type of boxplot that we recommend for common use. In this case, the upper whisker for Group 1 extends only to the most extreme observation within the $1.5 \times IQR$ limit, which is 59. Because there are no other outliers, the other whiskers extend to the extreme observations.

The Group 2 distribution appears to be more skewed: the upper whisker is longer than the lower whisker, and the upper end of the box (the third quartile) is farther from the mean than the lower end. The Group 1 distribution is reasonably symmetric when the outliers are ignored, as the stemplot in Unit 2 shows in more detail.

**3.3** (a) In a skewed distribution, the mean moves away from the median in the direction of the long tail. In this case, the mean household income is larger than the median income.
(b) The standard deviation cannot be negative, so the value reported is impossible.

# UNIT 4
# NORMAL DISTRIBUTIONS

## LESSON OVERVIEW

Histograms and stemplots give a quite detailed picture of a distribution. In this unit you will see that the overall pattern of a distribution can often be described compactly by a smooth curve, called a **density curve**. Think of a density curve as a smooth curve drawn through the tops of the bars of a relative frequency histogram. A density curve is usually an idealized description of a distribution that gives the overall pattern but ignores the irregularities that are present in actual data. In the video program, density curves are used to compare the distributions of the age of Americans in 1930 and in 2075. Of course, the second distribution is an estimate made by the Census Bureau. This is an effective use of density curves because we are interested in the big picture of changes in the overall distributions of age, not in small details.

The median of a distribution can be located on a density curve as the point that divides the curve into two equal areas. The mean of the distribution is the point at which the curve would balance if made out of solid material. Because a density curve represents an ideal distribution, we use a special symbol for its mean, the Greek letter $\mu$. The standard deviation is similarly represented by the Greek letter $\sigma$. The standard deviation $\sigma$ cannot be located by eye on most density curves. The mean and median are equal for symmetric density curves, but the mean of a skewed curve is located farther toward the long tail than the median.

The **normal distributions** are specified by bell-shaped symmetric density curves. Normal distributions are very common in statistics, so we will study their properties in detail. Unlike most distributions, a normal distribution is completely described by its mean $\mu$ and standard deviation $\sigma$. Both $\mu$ and $\sigma$ can be found from the shape of a normal curve. Changing $\mu$ moves a normal curve along the axis without changing its shape. Changing $\sigma$ changes the shape; curves with larger standard deviations $\sigma$ are more spread out and less sharply peaked. As the video notes, normal distributions give an approximate description of the overall pattern of many common types of data. But do remember that no distribution for actual data will be exactly normal. The smooth normal curve is an ideal distribution that is easy to work with, not an exact description.

All normal distributions are the same when measurements are made in units of $\sigma$ about the mean. These are called **standardized measurements**. In particular, all normal distributions satisfy the **68–95–99.7 rule**. This rule says that in any normal distribution, 68% of the observations fall within $\sigma$ of the mean $\mu$, 95% fall within two standard deviations of the mean, and 99.7% fall within $3\sigma$ on either side of $\mu$. Study Figure 1.16 in the text to get a clear picture of the situation. The 68–95–99.7 rule allows us to think about normal distributions without doing detailed calculations. In the video, we can quickly see how few young women are eligible for membership in a Beanstalk Club that is open only to women at least 5 feet 10 inches tall (and to men at least 6 feet 2 inches tall).

When we have several observations, each from a different normal distribution, we often use standardized measurements to compare the observations. As the video notes, the distribution of major league batting averages is roughly normal, but the standard deviation has changed over time. To compare how far outstanding hitters of different eras stood above their contemporaries, we standardize their batting averages.

## ASSIGNMENT

1. Read the LEARNING OBJECTIVES to see what specific skills you must acquire from this unit.

2. Read Section 1.3 of the text, starting at the beginning of the section and stopping at the heading "Normal Distribution Calculations."

3. Do the following problems from the SECTION 1.3 EXERCISES in the text: 1.72, 1.75, 1.77, 1.79.

4. Finally, try the SELF-TEST QUESTIONS and compare your answers with those given.

# LEARNING OBJECTIVES

## A. DENSITY CURVES

1. Know that areas under a density curve represent relative frequency, and that the total area under a density curve is 1.
2. Locate the median of a density curve by finding (approximately) the point that divides the area into two equal halves.
3. Locate the mean of a density curve by finding (approximately) the point at which the curve would balance.
4. Know that the mean and median both lie at the center of a symmetric density curve, and that the mean moves farther toward the long tail of a skewed curve.

## B. NORMAL DISTRIBUTIONS

1. Recognize the shape of normal curves and be able to estimate both the mean and standard deviation from such a curve.
2. Calculate a standardized observation from a normal distribution when given the original observation and the mean and standard deviation of the distribution.
3. Use the 68–95–99.7 rule and symmetry to state what percent of the observations from a normal distribution fall between two points when both points lie at the mean or one, two, or three standard deviations on either side of the mean.

## SELF-TEST QUESTIONS

**4.1** Figure 4.1 is the density curve of the distribution of the time to failure of an electronic component.
(a) What is the area under this curve?
(b) Which of the two points marked on the curve is the mean and which is the median? Explain your choice.

Figure 4.1

Time

**4.2** Measurements of the forehead breadth of a large number of Hungarian male skulls show that the distribution is approximately described by the normal curve in Figure 4.2. What is the approximate mean of this normal distribution? What is the approximate standard deviation?

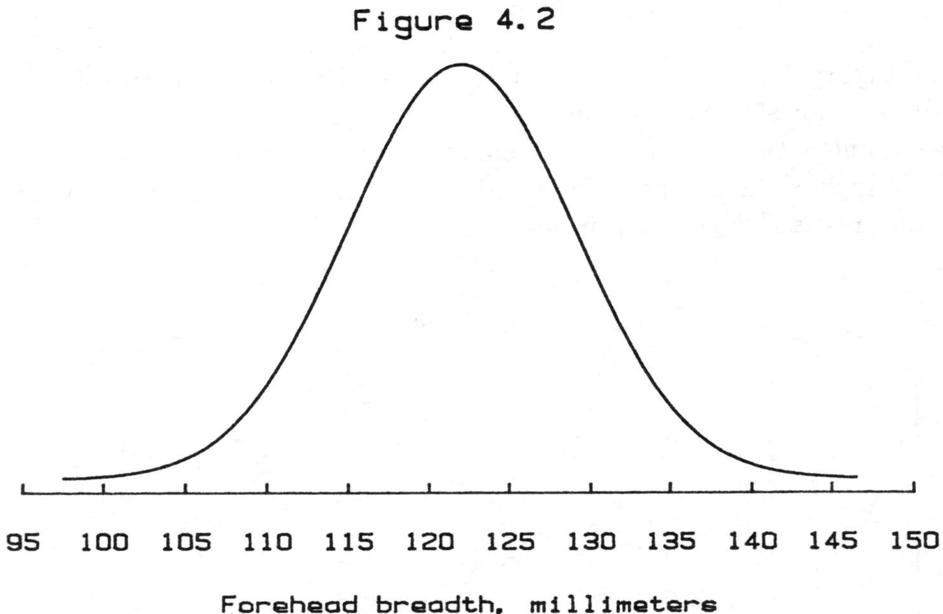


**4.3** Scores on the Wechsler Adult Intelligence Scale (a standard "IQ test") for the 20 to 34 age group are approximately normally distributed with mean $\mu = 110$ and standard deviation $\sigma = 25$.
(a) About what percent of people in this age group have scores above 110?
(b) About what percent have scores above 160?

**4.4** Sarah is 29 and her mother Ann is 62. Sarah scores 135 on the Wechsler Adult Intelligence Scale, while Ann scores 120. Wechsler scores for the 60 to 64 age group are approximately normally distributed with mean 90 and standard deviation 25.

(a) Use the information in Problem 4.3 to find Sarah's standardized score.
(b) Find Ann's standardized score, using the distribution for her age group. Which of the two has the higher score relative to her age group?

## SELF-TEST SOLUTIONS

**4.1** (a) Any density curve has exactly area 1 beneath it.
(b) The density curve in Figure 4.1 is strongly skewed to the right. (Because the time until the component fails cannot be less than 0, the entire area of the curve lies to the right of 0.) Therefore the mean is point B, the point more toward the long tail. The median is point A.

**4.2** Figure 4.3 shows the mean (at the center of the curve) and the point one standard deviation above the mean (the change of curvature point). The mean is about $\mu = 122$, and because the change of curvature point is about 129, the standard deviation is about $\sigma = 7$.

**4.3** (a) Because the mean and median of a normal curve are the same, 110 is the median. So 50% of the age group have IQ scores above 110.
(b) A score of 160 is two standard deviations above the mean. By the 95 part of the 68–95–99.7 rule, 95% of the scores fall between $\mu - 2\sigma$ and $\mu + 2\sigma$, or between 60 and 160. Of the 5% that fall outside this range, half are high and half are low because the normal curves are symmetric. So 2.5% have scores above 160. This problem illustrates how the symmetry of the normal curves and the 68–95–99.7 rule are

used together.

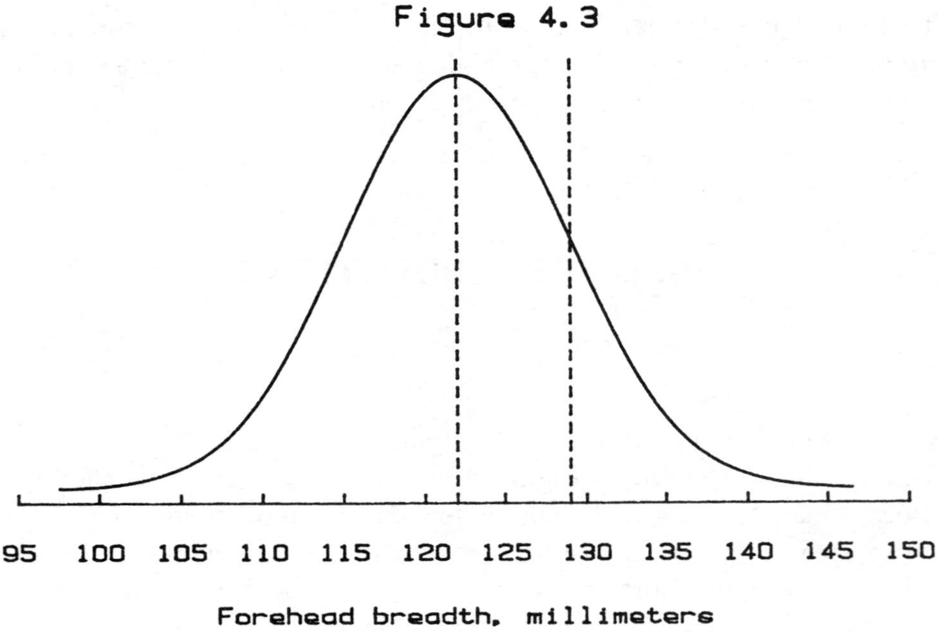


**4.4** (a) Sarah's standardized score is found by subtracting the mean and dividing by the standard deviation for her age group:

$$\begin{aligned} z &= \frac{x - \mu}{\sigma} \\ &= \frac{135 - 110}{25} = 1 \end{aligned}$$

That is, her score is one standard deviation above the mean for her age group.
(b) Ann's standardized score is found by using the mean and standard

deviation for the 60 to 64 age group:

$$\begin{aligned} z &= \frac{x - \mu}{\sigma} \\ &= \frac{120 - 90}{25} = 1.2 \end{aligned}$$

Therefore Ann stands higher relative to her age group than does Sarah, even though Sarah's actual score is higher.

# UNIT 5
# NORMAL CALCULATIONS

## LESSON OVERVIEW

Although the 68–95–99.7 rule allows us to make quick approximate calculations about normal distributions, we sometimes need more exact methods. This unit shows in detail how to answer two types of questions for any normal distribution. First, given an interval of possible outcomes, what is its relative frequency? Second, given a relative frequency such as "the highest 5% of the outcomes," what is the value with that relative frequency above or below it?

The video program asks and answers the following questions to illustrate normal distribution calculations of the first type: The heights of young women are normally distributed with mean $\mu = 65.5$ inches and standard deviation $\sigma = 2.5$ inches; what percent of these women are taller than 61.7 inches? The heights of 7 year-old girls are normally distributed with $\mu = 48.7$ inches and $\sigma = 1.9$ inches; what percent are shorter than 48.5 inches? The distribution of nitrogen oxide emissions from a prototype engine is estimated to be normal with $\mu = 0.78$ grams per mile and $\sigma = 0.525$ grams per mile; what percent of these cars will exceed the regulatory limit of 1.0 grams per mile? The distribution of blood cholesterol levels among adults is normal with $\mu = 213$ and $\sigma = 48.4$; what percent of the population fall in the borderline risk group with levels between 200 and 250?

The second type of calculation is illustrated by a question asked by the army in deciding which soldiers need custom-made helmets: the head circumferences of soldiers are approximately normal with $\mu = 22.8$ inches and $\sigma = 1.1$ inches; what head circumference is exceeded by just 5% of all soldiers?

Both types of calculation use the fact that all normal distributions are the same when a standardized scale is used. Now we state this fact more exactly. If X has the $N(\mu, \sigma)$ distribution, then the **standardized variable** $Z = (X - \mu)/\sigma$ has the **standard normal** distribution $N(0, 1)$. Table A in the text gives relative frequencies of the events $Z < z$ for many values of $z$. Normal distribution calculations are done in two steps:

- First restate the problem in terms of a standard normal variable $Z$ by standardizing the original problem.
- Then use Table A to obtain the answer.

Because normal distributions are important in statistics, we need a way to assess whether the distribution of a set of data is approximately normal. This is best done by looking at a special graph called a **normal quantile plot**, which is available on most statistical software systems. Deviations of the points on such a plot from a straight line show deviations of the data from normality. You do not need to be able to make a normal quantile plot (unless you have software that does it automatically), only to interpret the plot. The video program shows normal quantile plots for heights of girls (close to normal), nitrogen oxide emissions from vehicles (roughly normal), and carbon monoxide emissions from the same vehicles (skewed to the right, so not normal).

## ASSIGNMENT

1. Read the LEARNING OBJECTIVES to see what specific skills you must acquire from this unit.

2. Read Section 1.3 of the text, beginning with the heading "Normal Distribution Calculations" and continuing to the end of the chapter.

3. Do the following problems from the SECTION 1.3 EXERCISES in the text: 1.81, 1.83, 1.85, 1.93, 1.97, 1.98.

4. Finally, try the SELF-TEST QUESTIONS and compare your answers with those given.

## LEARNING OBJECTIVES

A. Given that a variable $X$ has the normal distribution with a stated mean $\mu$ and standard deviation $\sigma$, calculate the relative frequency of values above a stated number, below a stated number, or between two stated numbers.

B. Given that a variable $X$ has the normal distribution with a stated mean $\mu$ and standard deviation $\sigma$, calculate the point having a stated relative frequency above it. Also calculate the point having a stated relative frequency below it.

C. Given the normal quantile plot of a set of data, assess whether or not the distribution is approximately normal. Recognize right and left skewness, and also granularity due to imprecise measurement.

## SELF-TEST QUESTIONS

**5.1** The army reports that the distribution of head circumference among soldiers is approximately normal with mean 22.8 inches and standard deviation 1.1 inches.
(a) What percent of soldiers have head circumference greater than 24.5 inches?
(b) What percent of soldiers have head circumference between 20 inches and 25 inches?

**5.2** The army plans to provide custom-made helmets for soldiers whose head circumference falls in the top 1% of the distribution given in the previous problem. What head circumferences (in inches) fall in the top 1%?

**5.3** After a change is made in the design of an augmenter pump for aircraft hydraulic systems, tests show that the pump bearings are failing earlier than desired. Figure 5.1 is a normal quantile plot of the failure times of eight of these pumps. Is the distribution of failure times approximately normal? If not, what kind of deviation from normality is present?

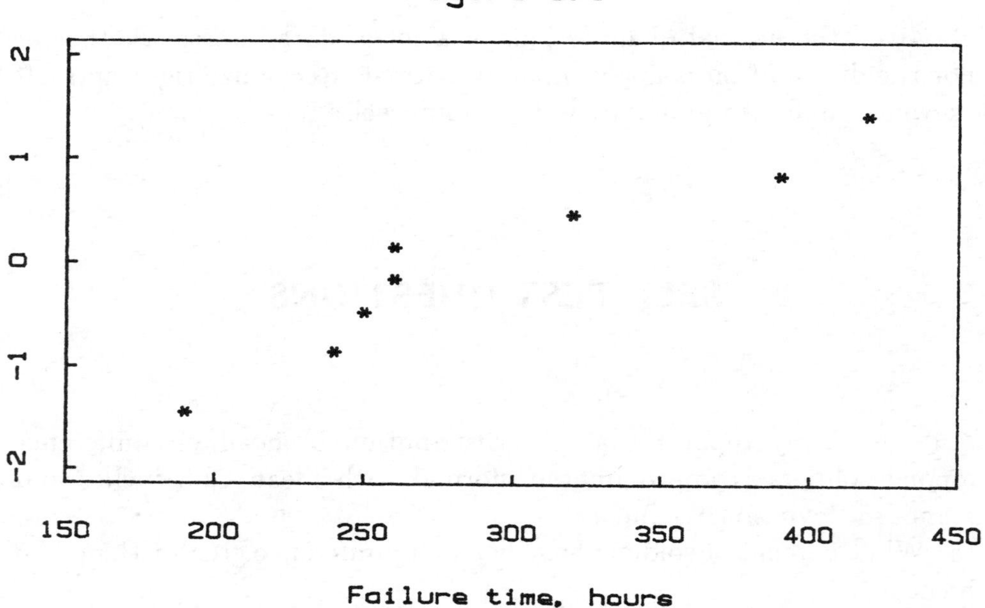


## SELF-TEST SOLUTIONS

**5.1** (a) Let $X$ be the head circumference of a soldier. We want the relative frequency of the event that

$$X > 24.5$$

After formulating the problem, standardize by subtracting the mean head circumference and dividing by the standard deviation. This changes $X$ into a standard normal variable $Z$. The problem becomes

$$\frac{X - 22.8}{1.1} > \frac{24.5 - 22.8}{1.1}$$
$$Z > 1.55$$

Now refer to Table A of the standard normal distribution. The table shows that the relative frequency *below* $z = 1.55$ is 0.9394. (This is the area under the standard normal density curve to the left of 1.55.) The relative frequency *above* 1.55 is therefore

$$1 - 0.9394 = 0.0606$$

or 6.06%.

(b) Follow the same steps. First formulate the problem: We want the relative frequency that

$$20 \leq X \leq 25$$

Then standardize to convert to a standard normal problem

$$\frac{20 - 22.8}{1.1} \leq Z \leq \frac{25 - 22.8}{1.1}$$
$$-2.55 \leq Z \leq 2.00$$

Table A shows that the area under the standard normal curve to the left of

$$z = -2.55 \quad \text{is} \quad 0.0054$$
$$z = 2.00 \quad \text{is} \quad 0.9772$$

The relative frequency between these points is the difference

$$0.9772 - 0.0054 = 0.9718$$

or 97.18%. Figure 5.2 illustrates this calculation.

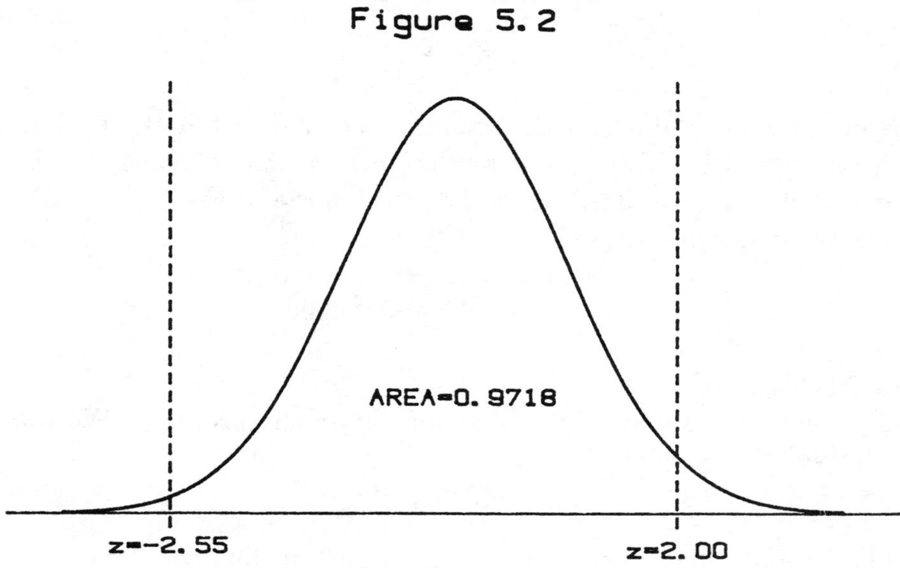


**5.2** We must find the head circumference $x$ such that just 1% of the distribution falls above it. That is, $x$ is the number such that the there is area 0.01 to the right of $x$ under the $N(22.8, 1.1)$ density curve. First use Table A to find the point $z$ with area 0.01 above it under the standard normal curve. Look for 0.99 (the area below the point) in the body of the table. The closest entry is .9901, which is the entry for $z = 2.33$. Now rewrite the equation for standardizing the variable $X$,

$$Z = \frac{X - 22.8}{1.1}$$

to give $x$ in terms of $z$

$$\begin{aligned} x &= 22.8 + 1.1 \times z \\ &= 22.8 + (1.1)(2.33) = 25.36 \end{aligned}$$

This is the value of $X$ with area 0.01 above it.

**5.3** The pattern in the normal quantile plot in Figure 5.1 bends to the right. To see the bend clearly, place a straightedge along the five earliest failure times and notice that the three later points fall to the right of the straightedge. The distribution is not approximately normal, but is skewed to the right.

# UNIT 6
# TIME SERIES

## LESSON OVERVIEW

This unit shows how to examine data that are measurements of the same variable at regular intervals of time. You will learn that such **time series** can show long-term **trends**, more or less regular up and down **cycles**, and regular **seasonal variation** as well as irregular fluctuations. You will also learn that these patterns can be made clearer by averaging over many individuals at one time or by averaging over time. Averaging in these ways is called **smoothing** the data.

The video begins by looking at circadian rhythms, the daily cycles of biological activity apparent in the behavior of many living things. You will see how experiments with people kept isolated from the light of day help uncover the working of our biological clocks. Plots of time series of measurements are a basic tool in such studies.

A second biological example will look at the patterns of brain activity induced by a sentence with a nonsense ending. The overall pattern becomes visible only when we average over the responses to many sentences. This illustrates the effectiveness of smoothing.

A similar kind of smoothing is used to create stock market indexes, which are averages of the prices of many individual stocks. You will hear the author of a stock market newsletter argue that the market has regular cycles that can be predicted, and Dean Burton Malkiel of Yale's business school say that there is no solid evidence for regular market cycles. You will learn to see patterns over time more clearly by using **running medians** of three or five consecutive observations.

**Note:** The text does not describe how to smooth a time series by running medians of three. The idea behind the most common smoothing methods is to replace each value of the time series by the center of several adjacent values. The centers fluctuate more slowly than the individual observations, but still respond to long-term changes. Because of the resistance of the median, medians of adjacent values are good smoothers.

**Running median of three**

**The running median of three smooths a time series by replacing each data point by the median of the point itself and the observations immediately before and after it in time order. Leave the first and last values, which are not the center of three, unchanged.**

The name describes the way in which the operation of finding medians "runs" along the sequence of data. For example, let us smooth Newcomb's measurements of the passage time of light (Table 1.1 on page 3 in the text). Figure 1.3 on page 16 in the text is a time plot of these data. The first few measurements in time order are

28 26 33 24 34 −44 27 16 40 ...

The running medians of three that smooth these observations are

28 28 26 33 34 34 27 27 ...

## ASSIGNMENT

1. Read the LEARNING OBJECTIVES to see what specific skills you must acquire from this unit.

2. Read the subsection on **Time Plots** at the end of Section 1.1 of the text.

3. Do the following problems from the SECTION 1.1 EXERCISES in the text: 1.32, 1.33. Then smooth the data in problem 1.32 by running medians of three and draw the smoothed data on the same graph as the original observations. Did smoothing emphasize the most interesting feature of these data?

4. Finally, try the SELF-TEST QUESTIONS and compare your answers with those given.

## LEARNING OBJECTIVES

A. Be able to detect trends, cycles, and seasonal variation in the plot of a time series.

B. Recognize that the time plot of an average over many individuals is usually smoother (shows the overall pattern more clearly) than the time plot for a single individual.

C. Be able to smooth a time series by computing running medians of three consecutive observations.

## SELF-TEST QUESTIONS

**6.1** What is the difference between *seasonal variation* and *cycles* in a time series?

The Consumer Price Index (CPI) measures the cost of a fixed "market basket" of goods and services that represent the items purchased by urban American households. A rise in the CPI shows that prices are rising. Here is a table of the percent increase in the CPI for the 20 years 1971 to 1990.

| Year | 1971 | 1972 | 1973 | 1974 | 1975 | 1976 | 1977 | 1978 |
|---|---|---|---|---|---|---|---|---|
| % Change | 4.1 | 6.2 | 11.0 | 9.1 | 5.8 | 6.5 | 7.6 | 11.4 |
| Year | 1979 | 1980 | 1981 | 1982 | 1983 | 1984 | 1985 | 1986 |
| % Change | 13.5 | 10.2 | 6.0 | 3.0 | 3.4 | 3.5 | 1.5 | 5.1 |
| Year | 1987 | 1988 | 1989 | 1990 | | | | |
| % Change | 3.6 | 4.1 | 4.8 | 5.4 | | | | |

**6.2** Make a plot of the annual percentage change in the CPI against time. Describe the important patterns that you see in this time series.

**6.3** Smooth this time series by running medians of three. Plot the smoothed time series on the same graph as the original (use a different color or a different plotting symbol). Are the patterns that you saw still present in the smoothed time series?

## SELF-TEST SOLUTIONS

**6.1** Cycles are up and down movements in a time series that recur over time but may be *irregular* in strength and duration. Seasonal variation, on the other hand, produces *regular* cycles that are tied to the calendar. The strength of the up and down movements in seasonal variation is often irregular, but the duration is regular. The stock market goes up and down (has cycles), but these are not predictable. Retail sales go up every December and down after Christmas; they display seasonal variation.

**6.2** The time series plot of the annual percent change in the CPI appears in Figure 6.1 as points connected by solid lines. There is no consistent trend over this period. There are two strong up and down cycles in the 1970s, a period of generally high inflation. Inflation was lower in the 1980s; but two shallow cycles and the upward slope of a third can be discerned. As in most real time series, the patterns here are not perfectly regular, so that there is no one "right answer" in describing what you see.

**6.3** The first and last points in the series are left unchanged because they do not have points on both sides of them. The running median at the second point (1972) is the median of 4.1, 6.2, and 11.0, which is

6.2. The next running median is the median of 6.2, 11.0, and 9.1, and so on. The consecutive running medians of three are

| | | | | | | | | | |
|---|---|---|---|---|---|---|---|---|---|
| 4.1 | 6.2 | 9.1 | 9.1 | 6.5 | 6.5 | 7.6 | 11.4 | 11.4 | 10.2 |
| 6.0 | 3.4 | 3.4 | 3.4 | 3.5 | 3.6 | 4.1 | 4.1 | 4.8 | 5.4 |

The running medians appear in Figure 6.1 connected by dashed lines. The graph of the running medians brings down the peaks in the original data and in fact smooths out all traces of cycles in the 1980s. But it makes it clearer that prices were rising faster before 1980 than afterwards. Smoothing over time tends to hide shorter-term patterns and emphasize long term patterns.

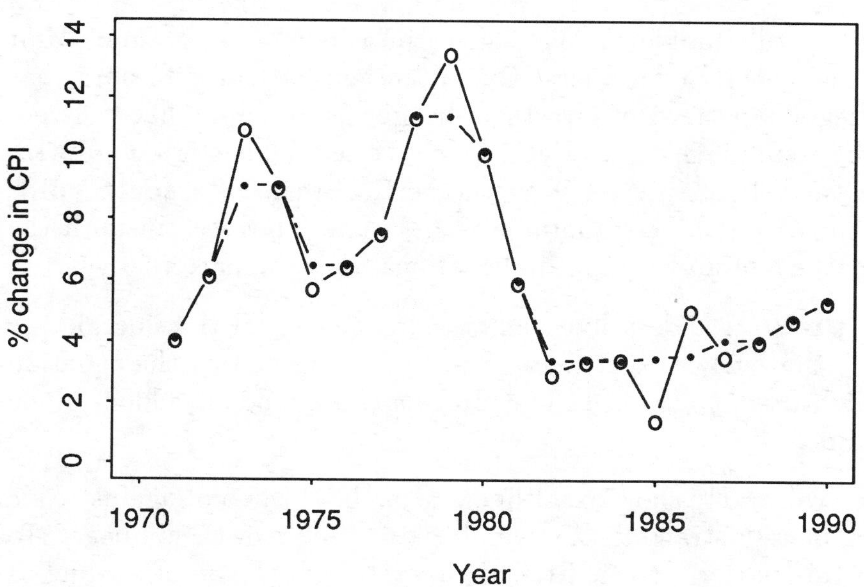

# UNIT 7
# MODELS FOR GROWTH

## LESSON OVERVIEW

Like Unit 6, this unit looks at changes in a variable over time. Unit 6 concerned general time series. Our attention now turns to data that show a regular pattern of growth over time, so regular that it is described by a simple mathematical model. To see the pattern of growth, plot the variable of interest $y$ on the vertical scale of a **scatterplot** against time $t$ on the horizontal scale. We are interested in both the overall pattern of growth and in deviations from the pattern.

**Linear growth** adds a fixed amount in each equal time period. A variable $y$ that shows exact linear growth is described by the equation of a straight line, $y = a + bt$. The **slope** $b$ is the amount added in one unit of time.

Real data will rarely show exact linear growth. If the plot against time is approximately straight, the overall pattern of growth is linear. To describe this pattern, **fit a line** to the data. That is, pass a line as closely as possible through the points. You can do this by eye, or you can use the least-squares method. The details of how to calculate a least-squares line are given in the next unit; only the idea appears in this unit. Linear growth is illustrated in the video by the increase in the height of young children.

The deviations from the overall pattern of linear growth are described by the **residuals**. A plot of the residuals against time magnifies the deviations for easier inspection. Look for outlying points and for systematic patterns in the residuals.

If you are satisfied that linear growth describes the overall pattern of the data, you can use the fitted line for **prediction**. Prediction outside the time interval for which you have data is called **extrapolation**. The results of extrapolation are often untrustworthy.

**Exponential growth** multiplies by a fixed amount in each equal time period. You can see the shape of the **exponential curves** by multiplying repeatedly by the same number and plotting the results. Compound interest produces exponential growth. Real data rarely show exact exponential growth, but may show a pattern of approximate exponential growth. The example used in the video is the number of acres defoliated by gypsy moths in successive years of an infestation.

You can check whether a variable $y$ has the overall pattern of exponential growth by taking the **logarithm of each value**. Use a calculator to find logarithms. Plot the logarithms against time. If the logarithms of $y$ show an approximate linear pattern, $y$ itself is approximately exponential. You can fit a straight line to the logarithms to describe exponential growth. The residuals from this line describe the deviations from the exponential pattern. If you are satisfied that the line fits the logarithms adequately, you can use it for prediction. The video briefly discusses an example that is presented in more detail in the text: the growth in world oil production over time.

**Note:** Some of the reading in the text is the same for this unit and Unit 8, which you may want to study together. The text follows a slightly different order than the video units. For this unit, you can skip the section on scatterplots and ignore the details of calculating the least-squares line. The scatterplots in this unit are just time plots, which you have already met. Unit 8 concentrates on general scatterplots and least-squares regression.

## ASSIGNMENT

1. Read the LEARNING OBJECTIVES to see what specific skills you must acquire from this unit.

2. Read Section 2.2 of the text, omitting the subsections on "Least-Squares Regression" and on "Outliers and Influential Observations." Read Section 2.3 of the text.

3. Do the following problems from the SECTION 2.2 EXERCISES in the text: 2.16, 2.21. Also do the following problems from the SECTION 2.3 EXERCISES in the text: 2.37, 2.41.

4. Finally, try the SELF-TEST QUESTIONS and compare your answers with those given.

# LEARNING OBJECTIVES

## A. LINEAR GROWTH

1. Properties of straight lines (Review).

   (a) Explain what the slope $b$ and the intercept $a$ mean in the equation $y = a + bt$ of a straight line.

   (b) Draw a graph of the straight line $y = a + bt$ when you are given the equation.

2. Examining a plot against time

   (a) Recognize an overall pattern of linear growth in a graph of a variable $y$ against time.

   (b) Describe the pattern by a straight line drawn by eye on the graph.

   (c) Recognize important deviations from linear growth such as outlying observations and a curved pattern.

3. Using a fitted line

   (a) Predict $y$ for a given time $t$, either from the equation of the fitted line or from a graph of the line.

   (b) Recognize extrapolation and be aware of its dangers.

4. Residuals

   (a) Compute a residual when given the observed value and the predicted value of $y$ for a time $t$.

   (b) Make a residual plot from the residuals and use this plot to see deviations from the linear pattern.

## B. EXPONENTIAL GROWTH

1. Exact exponential growth

   (a) Recognize situations in which exponential growth is occurring due to repeated multiplication by the same number.

   (b) Recognize the general shape of exponential curves.

2. Examining a plot against time

   (a) Recognize an exponential pattern by taking logarithms, plotting the logarithms against time, and recognizing a linear pattern.

   (b) Recognize major deviations from exponential growth by looking at the residuals of the logarithms from linear growth.

   (c) Predict $\log y$ when given a line fitted to the plot of the logarithms, and then predict $y$ by $y = 10^{\log y}$.

# SELF-TEST QUESTIONS

**7.1** Jason appears to be growing slowly as a toddler. His height between 18 and 30 months of age increases as follows.

| Age (months) | Height (cm) |
|---|---|
| 18 | 76.5 |
| 21 | 78.7 |
| 24 | 82.0 |
| 27 | 84.8 |
| 30 | 86.0 |

(a) Make a graph of Jason's height against his age. Do the data show a clear linear pattern so that you are willing to use a fitted line as an overall description?
(b) The least-squares regression line fitted to these data is

$$y = 61.5 + 0.837t$$

Plot this line on your graph from (a).
(c) According to this line, how much does Jason grow each month? If this line described Jason's growth from birth, what would be his height at birth? (In fact, growth is not linear in the early months of life, so the line does not describe birth height.)
(d) Use the fitted line to predict Jason's height at age 2 years. Then calculate the residual for this age. Where do the residuals appear in your graph from (b)?
(e) Would you be willing to use the fitted line to predict Jason's height at age 21 years? Explain your answer.

**7.2** A rural landowner has a pond with area 50,000 square feet (just over an acre). One day he notices a growth of algae in one corner of the pond, covering 8 square feet. The algae doubles its area each day.
(a) How much area does the algae occupy 10 days later?
(b) At this point the landowner becomes concerned because about 16% of the pond is covered with algae. How many more days will the algae take to cover the entire pond?

**7.3** Technology sometimes advances exponentially. Self-propelled naval torpedos were invented in 1866 by the Englishman Robert Whitehead. Here are the ranges (in yards) of torpedos made by Whitehead's company in the years before the first world war. (Data from the appendix of Edwin A. Gray, *The Devil's Device*, London, 1975.)

| Year | Torpedo range |
|---|---|
| 1866 | 220 |
| 1876 | 600 |
| 1905 | 2190 |
| 1906 | 6560 |
| 1913 | 18,590 |

(a) Plot range against year. Then plot the logarithm of range against year. Why can we conclude that torpedo ranges during these years showed approximately exponential growth?
(b) Do any individual years appear to be outliers from the overall pattern?
(c) The least-squares line, calculated omitting the data for 1905, is

$$\log y = -70.58 + 0.03909t$$

Plot this line on your graph of logarithms against year in (a). Then use this line to predict the range in 1905.

## SELF-TEST SOLUTIONS

**7.1** (a) The plot of height against age appears in Figure 7.1. The overall pattern is clearly linear, so that a straight line is a good description.
(b) To graph the line, choose two values of $t$, say $t = 20$ and $t = 30$. Then use the equation to calculate the corresponding values of $y$. For $t = 20$,

$$y = 61.5 + (0.837)(20) = 78.2$$

and for $t = 30$

$$y = 61.5 + (0.837)(30) = 86.6$$

Now plot the two points (20, 78.2) and (30, 86.6) on the graph and use a straightedge to connect them with a straight line. This is the line you want. It appears in Figure 7.1.

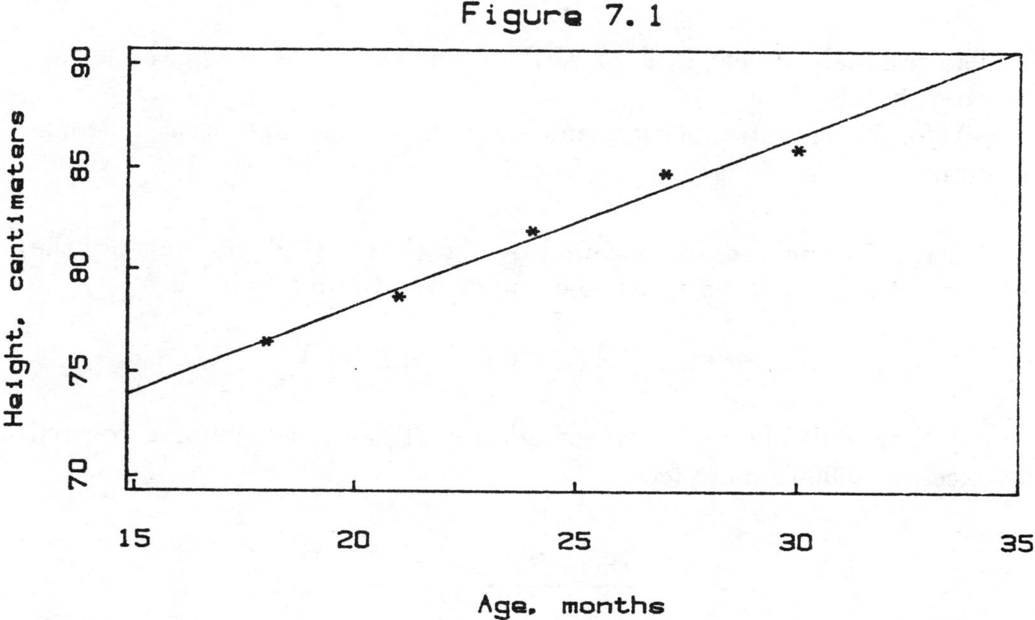


(c) The amount added per month is the slope of the line, 0.837 cm. Jason's height at birth ($t = 0$) would be given by the intercept of the line, 61.5 cm, if the line described his growth from birth.

(d) To predict the height at 2 years, convert 2 years to 24 months because we are measuring time in months. Then substitute $t = 24$ into the equation of the line. The result is

$$y = 61.5 + (0.837)(24) = 81.6 \text{ cm}$$

The observed value at 24 months was 82.0 cm, so the residual is

$$\begin{aligned}\text{residual} &= \text{observed} - \text{predicted} \\ &= 82.0 - 81.6 = 0.4\end{aligned}$$

The residuals appear in Figure 7.1 as vertical deviations of the points from the fitted line.
(e) No. This is extrapolation, and is certainly wrong in this case. People do not grow at the same rate from 30 months to 21 years.

**7.2** (a) To find the area covered by algae after 10 days, multiply the original area by 2 ten times. The quick way to do this is

$$8 \times 2^{10} = 8 \times 1024 = 8192 \text{ sq ft}$$

(b) Now multiply by 2 for each additional day until the area covered exceeds 50,000 square feet:

| Day | Square Feet |
|---|---|
| 1 | 16,384 |
| 2 | 32,768 |
| 3 | 65,536 |

The pond will be covered before the end of the third day after the landowner becomes concerned. This again illustrates the rapidity of exponential growth.

**7.3** (a) Figure 7.2 is a plot of range against year, while Figure 7.3 plots the logarithm of range against year. The common logarithm (base 10, "LOG" button on most calculators) was used. Figure 7.3 is much closer to a linear pattern than Figure 7.2. The growth is roughly exponential because the plot of the logarithms against time is roughly linear.

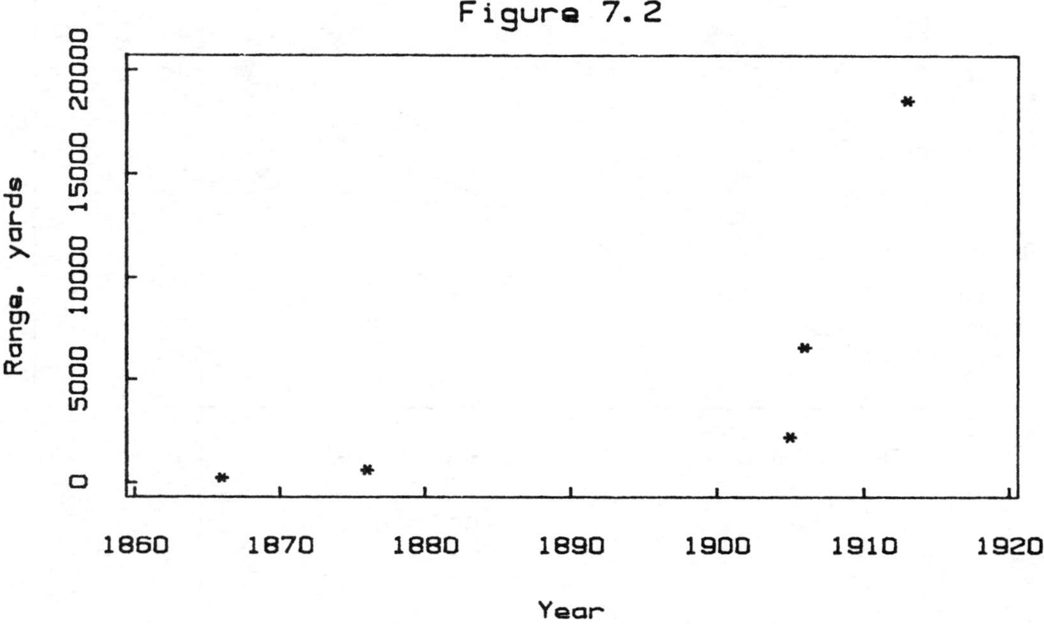


(b) The point for the year 1905 is an outlier. It is clearly below the line formed by the other four points in Figure 7.3. (The large gap in the data between 1876 and 1905 makes it uncertain that growth was exponential during the missing years, though four of the five points available fit the exponential model well. It is possible that 1905 marks the end of a slow-growth period.)

(c) To draw the line, it is simplest to find two points and connect them. For example, the predicted values of the logarithm of the range for 1880 is

$$\log y = -70.58 + (0.03909)(1880) = 2.91$$

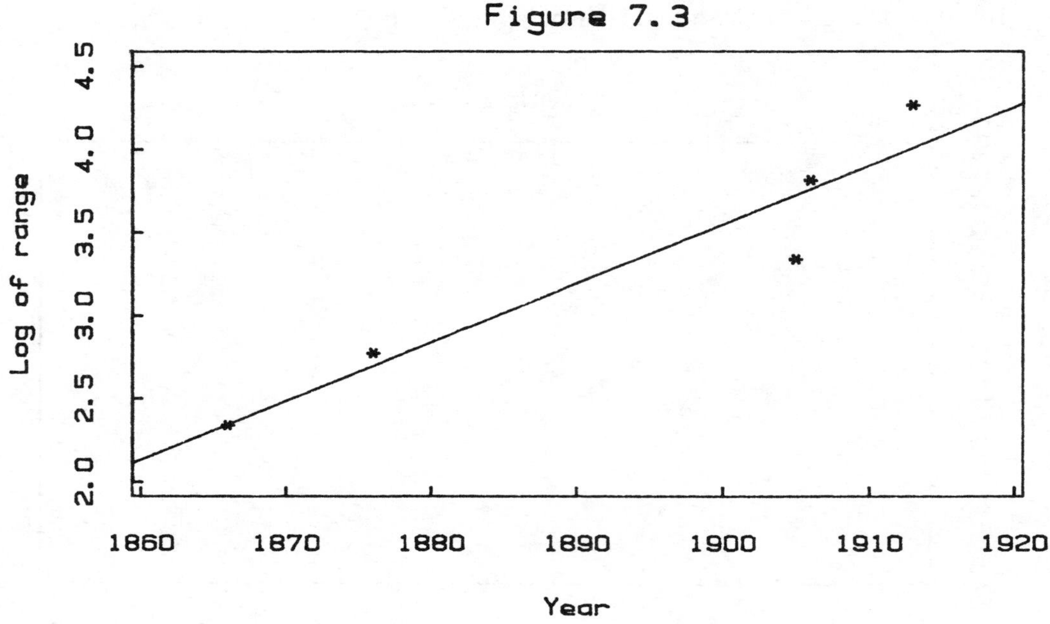


and the value for 1910 is

$$\log y = -70.58 + (0.03909)(1910) = 4.08$$

Therefore (1880, 2.91) and (1910, 4.08) are two points on the line. The least-squares line appears in Figure 7.3. The predicted value for 1905 is found by first calculating the predicted value of the logarithm from the equation of the fitted line

$$\log y = -70.58 + (0.03909)(1905) = 3.886$$

and then

$$\begin{aligned} y &= 10^{\log y} \\ &= 10^{3.886} = 7699 \text{ yards} \end{aligned}$$

(This answer was obtained by using the power key on a calculator without rounding the value of $\log y$. You will get a slightly different answer if you use the rounded value 3.886. You should avoid rounding intermediate steps in a calculation whenever possible.)

# UNIT 8
# DESCRIBING RELATIONSHIPS

## LESSON OVERVIEW

In Units 6 and 7 we looked at the change or growth in a variable over time. This unit concerns relationships between two variables, especially between two quantitative variables. A **quantitative variable** takes numerical values for which arithmetic operations make sense. Other variables are **categorical variables** that record into which of two or more groups an observation falls. In many of the examples we will study, changes in a variable $x$ are thought to explain or even cause changes in a second variable $y$. In such examples, $x$ is called an **explanatory variable** and $y$ is called a **response variable**.

A **scatterplot** is a plot of observations on quantitative variables $x$ and $y$ as points in the plane. The explanatory variable, if any, is always plotted on the horizontal scale of a scatterplot. A time plot is just a scatterplot with time as the explanatory variable. The video contains several examples of scatterplots. One shows the relationship between the number $y$ of manatees killed by boats and the number $x$ of power boats registered in Florida over a period of 11 years. Another shows the fluoride content $x$ of water supplies and the number $y$ of dental cavities in children for several cities. A third scatterplot pictures the lean body weight $x$ and base metabolism weight $y$ for several subjects in a study of obesity. In each of these examples, $x$ helps explain $y$. Plotting points with different symbols allows us to see the effect of a categorical variable in a scatterplot. In the video, large and small cities are distinguished by different symbols in the fluoride example.

In examining a scatterplot, look for an overall pattern showing the form, direction, and strength of the relationship, and then for outliers or other deviations from this pattern. **Linear** (straight line) relationships are an important form. If the relationship has a clear direction, we speak of **positive association** when both variables increase together or of **negative association** when an increase in one tends to accompany a decrease in the other.

Smoothing a scatterplot by a **median trace** helps reveal the nature of the dependence of $y$ on $x$. The median trace is found by slicing the scatterplot vertically like a loaf of bread, calculating the median $y$ within each slice, and plotting these medians connected by straight lines. In the video, the negative association between draft number $y$ in the 1970 draft lottery and birth date $x$ becomes clear from a median trace.

When a scatterplot suggests that the dependence of $y$ on $x$ can be summarized by a straight line, the **least squares regression line** of $y$ on $x$ can be calculated. This is the most important calculation in this unit. The video calculates the least squares regression line of metabolic rate $y$ on lean body mass $x$ for a group of subjects. This fitted line can be used to predict $y$ for a given value of $x$.

The fit of a regression line is examined by plotting the **residuals**, or differences between the observed and predicted values of $y$. Look for **outliers**, which are points with unusually large residuals. Also look for nonlinear patterns and uneven variation about the line. **Influential observations**, individual points that substantially change the regression line, must also be spotted and examined. Influential observations are often outliers in the $x$ variable, but may not have large residuals. Evidence of the effects of **lurking variables** on $y$ may be provided by plots of $y$ and the residuals against the time order of the observations.

**Note:** There are many recipes for the slope $b$ of the least-squares regression line. The recipe in the text, Equation (2.1) differs slightly from the recipe in the video. Divide both numerator and denominator of the video recipe by $n$ to get the text recipe. Both formulas give the same result.

## ASSIGNMENT

1. Read the LEARNING OBJECTIVES to see what specific skills you must acquire from this unit.

2. Read the introduction to Chapter 2 of the text and Sections 2.1 and 2.2. Concentrate on the parts of Section 2.2 not covered in Unit 7.

3. Do the following problems from the SECTION 2.1 EXERCISES in the text: 2.1, 2.3, 2.10, 2.12. Also do the following problems from the SECTION 2.2 EXERCISES in the text: 2.23, 2.25.

4. Finally, try the SELF-TEST QUESTIONS and compare your answers with those given.

# LEARNING OBJECTIVES

A. Recognize whether a variable is quantitative or categorical.

B. Identify the explanatory and response variables in situations where one variable explains or influences another.

C. SCATTERPLOTS

1. Make a scatterplot for two quantitative variables, placing the explanatory variable (if any) on the horizontal scale.
2. Add a categorical variable to the scatterplot by using several plotting symbols.
3. Recognize positive or negative association, a linear pattern, and outliers in a scatterplot.
4. Smooth an explanatory-response scatterplot by means of a median trace.

D. REGRESSION

1. Calculate the least squares regression line of $y$ on $x$ from data, using Equation (2.1) in the text.
2. Use the least squares regression line to predict $y$ for a given $x$.
3. Recognize outliers and potential influential observations from a scatterplot with the regression line drawn on it.

4. Calculate the residuals and plot them against $y$ and against the time order of the observations. Recognize unusual patterns.

## SELF-TEST QUESTIONS

**8.1** Identify each bold face variable below as quantitative or categorical, and also identify the explanatory and response variables in each setting.
(a) A political scientist believes that there is a "gender gap" in American voting, with women more likely to vote Democratic. She therefore interviews a random sample of voters and records the **sex** of the respondents and the **political party** of the candidate for whom they voted in the last presidential election.
(b) A study of the relationship between education and income records the **annual earned income** and the **years of school completed** of each of a large sample of subjects. In addition, the study records the **type of high school** attended (public, religious, or private nonreligious).

**8.2** The following table gives data on the lean body mass (kilograms) and resting metabolic rate for 12 women and 7 men who are subjects in a study of obesity. The researchers suspect that lean body mass (that is, the subject's weight leaving out all fat) is an important influence on metabolic rate.

| Subject | Sex | Mass | Rate | Subject | Sex | Mass | Rate |
|---|---|---|---|---|---|---|---|
| 1 | M | 62.0 | 1792 | 11 | F | 40.3 | 1189 |
| 2 | M | 62.9 | 1666 | 12 | F | 33.1 | 913 |
| 3 | F | 36.1 | 995 | 13 | M | 51.9 | 1460 |
| 4 | F | 54.6 | 1425 | 14 | F | 42.4 | 1124 |
| 5 | F | 48.5 | 1396 | 15 | F | 34.5 | 1052 |
| 6 | F | 42.0 | 1418 | 16 | F | 51.1 | 1347 |
| 7 | M | 47.4 | 1362 | 17 | F | 41.2 | 1204 |
| 8 | F | 50.6 | 1502 | 18 | M | 51.9 | 1867 |
| 9 | F | 42.0 | 1256 | 19 | M | 46.9 | 1439 |
| 10 | M | 48.7 | 1614 | | | | |

(a) Make a scatterplot of the data for the female subjects. Which is the explanatory variable?
(b) Is the association between these variables positive or negative? What is the overall shape of the relationship?
(c) Now add the data for the male subjects to your graph, using a different color or a different plotting symbol. Does the type of relationship that you observed in (b) hold for men also? How do the male subjects as a group differ from the female subjects as a group?
(d) Smooth your scatterplot (for all 19 subjects) by making a median trace. Slice lean body mass into 10-kilogram slices (30 to 40, 40 to 50, and so on) to make your median trace and draw it on your scatterplot.

**8.3** Many manatees in Florida are killed or injured by power boats. The table below gives data on power boat registrations (in thousands) and the number of manatees killed by boats in Florida in the years 1977–1987.
(a) Make a scatterplot of boat registrations and manatees killed. The overall relationship is roughly linear.
(b) Calculate the least squares regression line and draw it on your graph.

(c) Power boat registrations in 1990 increased to 719,000. Based on the data given here, predict the number of manatees killed by boats in 1990.
(d) Which point on the graph has the largest residual, either positive or negative? Calculate the residual for that point. Do you think that this point will be highly influential?

| Year | Boats | Manatees killed |
|---|---|---|
| 1977 | 447 | 13 |
| 1978 | 460 | 21 |
| 1979 | 481 | 24 |
| 1980 | 498 | 16 |
| 1981 | 513 | 24 |
| 1982 | 512 | 20 |
| 1983 | 526 | 15 |
| 1984 | 559 | 34 |
| 1985 | 585 | 33 |
| 1986 | 614 | 33 |
| 1987 | 645 | 39 |

## SELF-TEST SOLUTIONS

**8.1** (a) Both sex (male or female) and political party (Democrat, Republican, or other) are categorical variables. Because the political scientist thinks that the sex of a voter influences their party preference, sex is the explanatory variable and political party is the response variable.
(b) Both income (in dollars) and years of education are quantitative

variables. That is, they are measured in units for which arithmetic makes sense, unlike sex or political party. The type of high school is a categorical variable. We expect that years of schooling will influence income, so years of schooling is the explanatory variable and income is the response variable. (The type of high school may be related to either years of school completed or income; it is best thought of as another explanatory variable, but you need not be concerned about this.)

**8.2** (a) The explanatory variable is lean body mass, because the researchers believe that this influences metabolic rate. Body mass is therefore plotted on the horizontal scale in the scatterplot. The scatterplot appears in Figure 8.1. The asterisks are the data for the female subjects.
(b) The association is positive, because subjects with higher lean body mass also tend to have higher metabolic rates. Moreover, the relationship is roughly linear (straight line) in shape.
(c) The data for male subjects appear as open circles in Figure 8.1. The positive association and linear relationship continue to hold, although adding the men increases the scatter of the points about the linear trend for large masses. The men tend to have higher lean body masses and higher metabolic rates than the women (that is, men as a group are bigger than women). The four highest metabolic rates among the 19 subjects belong to men.
(d) Arranging the metabolic rate data within each slice in increasing order to compute the median gives: For 30 to 40 kilograms,

913 995 1052

and the median is 995. For 40 to 50 kilograms,

1124 1189 1204 1256 1362 1396 1418 1439 1614

with median 1362. For the 50 to 60 kilogram slice,

1347 1425 1460 1502 1867

so that the median is 1460. Finally, the two metabolic rates in the 60 to 70 kilogram slice are 1666 and 1792; their median is midway between these values, or 1729. Now plot these medians 995, 1362, 1460, 1729 vertically above the midpoints 35, 45, 55, 65 of the slices to form the median trace.

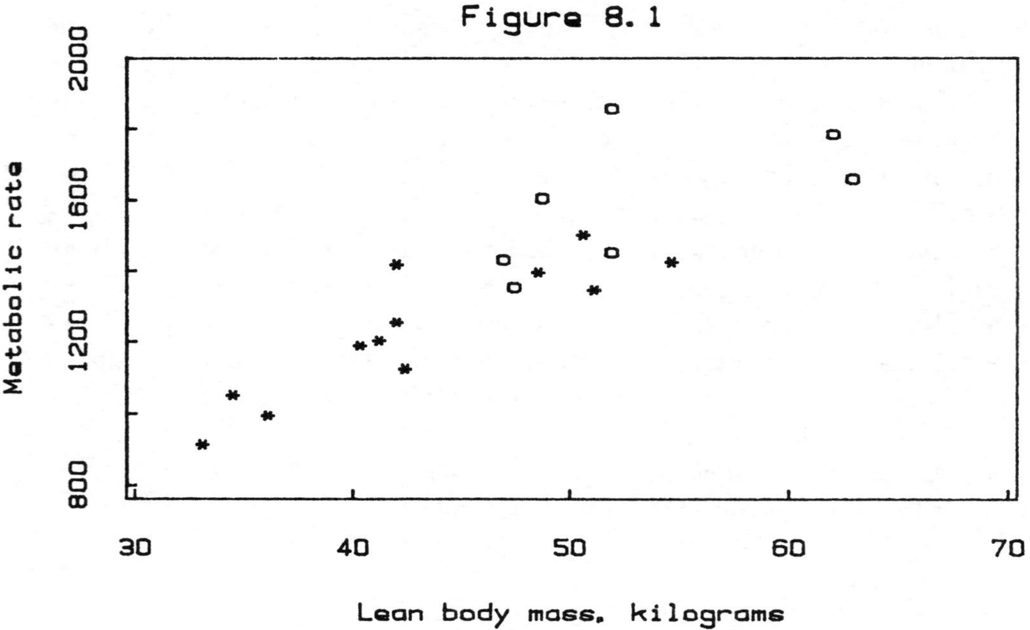


**8.3** (a) The scatterplot appears in Figure 8.2. Because boats kill manatees, the number of boat registrations is $x$, the horizontal (explanatory)

variable and the number of manatees killed by boats is $y$ the vertical (response) variable. This distinction is very important, because reversing the roles of the variables gives a different least squares line.

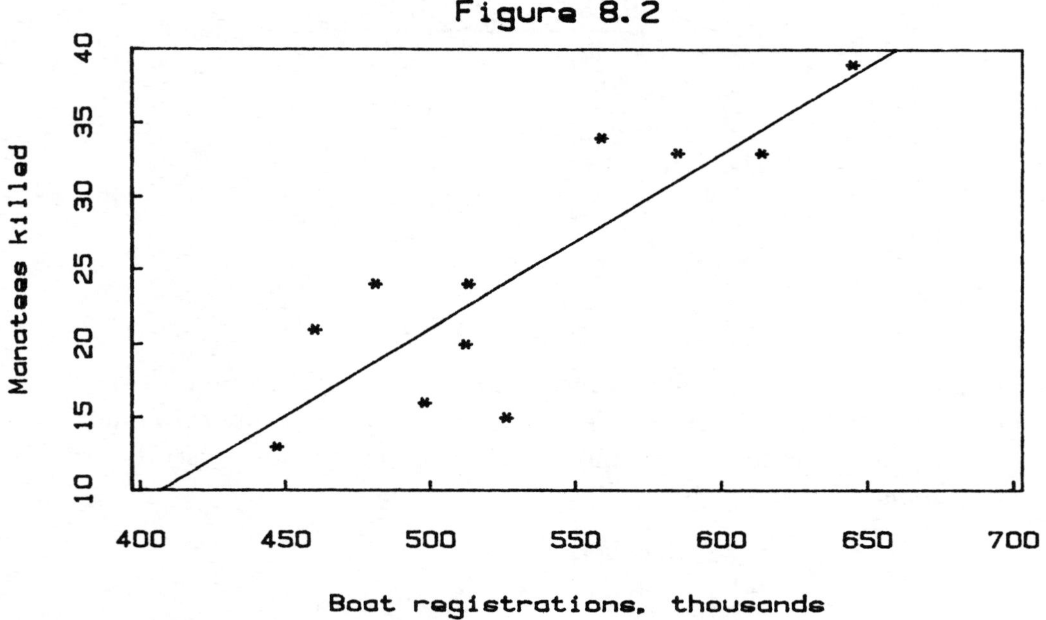


(b) To compute the least squares line with a basic calculator, follow the pattern of Example 2.9 in the text. The building block sums are:

$$\begin{aligned}
\sum x &= 447 + \cdots + 645 = 5840 \\
\sum x^2 &= 447^2 + \cdots + 645^2 = 3,140,490 \\
\sum y &= 13 + \cdots + 39 = 272 \\
\sum xy &= (447)(13) + \cdots + (645)(39) = 149,153
\end{aligned}$$

Then from Equation (2.1) of the text

$$\begin{aligned} b &= \frac{\sum xy - \frac{1}{n}(\sum x)(\sum y)}{\sum x^2 - \frac{1}{n}(\sum x)^2} \\ b &= \frac{149,153 - \frac{1}{11}(5840)(272)}{3,140,490 - \frac{1}{11}(5840)^2} \\ &= \frac{4745.727}{39,980.909} = 0.1187 \\ a &= \overline{y} - b\overline{x} \\ &= \frac{272}{11} - 0.1187\frac{5840}{11} = -38.29 \end{aligned}$$

The resulting line is

$$\hat{y} = -38.29 + 0.1187$$

It is shown in Figure 8.2 superimposed on the scatterplot. (c) The predicted response is found by substituting the given $x$ into the equation of the regression line. Remember that $x$ is power boat registrations in *thousands.*

$$\begin{aligned} \hat{y} &= -38.29 + 0.1187x \\ &= -38.29 + (.1187)(719) = 47.05 \end{aligned}$$

We predict that about 47 manatees were killed by boats in 1990. In fact, exactly 47 were killed. Regression will not usually give such accurate predictions.

(d) Study of the graph and the table reveals that the largest residual occurs in 1983, when only 15 manatees were killed. The point is below the line, so the residual is negative. The predicted response in 1983 is

$$\hat{y} = -38.29 + (.1187)(526) = 24.15$$

The numerical value of the residual is therefore

$$\text{residual} = \text{observed } y - \text{predicted } y$$

$$\begin{aligned} &= y - \hat{y} \\ &= 15 - 24.15 = -9.15 \end{aligned}$$

This point is *not* very influential; that is, removing this point will not change the position of the regression line very much. The reason is that the line must pass through the point $(\overline{x}, \overline{y})$. The value $x = 526$ for 1983 is close to $\overline{x} = 530.9$ so removing it will have little effect on the line unless the residual is extremely large. In this case the regression line for the 10 points omitting 1983 is

$$\hat{y} = -36.72 + 0.1175x$$

which is very close to the original line. Points that are extreme (far from $\overline{x}$) in the $x$ direction, on the other hand, are often very influential. They pull the line to themselves—so they have small residuals.

# UNIT 9
# CORRELATION

This unit contains two main segments. The first introduces the **correlation coefficient** $r$, an important measure of the strength and direction of the straight-line association between two quantitative variables. The video illustrates the use of correlation in describing the results of a study of identical twins who have been raised apart. These twins have a strong correlation between physical characteristics and, more surprisingly, a moderately strong correlation between mental and behavioral characteristics. Correlation always satisfies $-1 \leq r \leq 1$, and $r = \pm 1$ only in the case of perfect linear association. The value of $r$ is not affected by changes in the unit of measurement of either variable.

Recall that regression describes a straight-line relationship between an explanatory variable and a response variable. Correlation applies to any two quantitative variables; it does not require that one be an explanatory variable. When we have an explanatory variable and a response variable, however, correlation and regression are closely related. The second part of this unit describes the relationship between correlation and regression. The **squared correlation coefficient** $r^2$ is the fraction of the variance of one variable explained by least-squares regression on the other variable. The regression line of $y$ on $x$ is the line with slope $b = rs_y/s_x$ and passing through the point $(\overline{x}, \overline{y})$. In the television program, the Coleman Report uses $r^2$ to describe how characteristics of schools are surprisingly poor predictors of student achievement.

The results of computing a correlation or regression must be interpreted with due attention to the following: the possible effects of lurking variables, the lack of resistance of these procedures, the danger of extrapolation, the fact that correlations based on averages are usually too high for individuals, and an understanding that correlation and regression measure only linear relationships to the exclusion of other important aspects of the data.

## ASSIGNMENT

1. Read the LEARNING OBJECTIVES to see what specific skills you must acquire from this unit.

2. Read Section 2.4 of the text.

3. Do the following problems from the SECTION 2.4 EXERCISES in the text: 2.49, 2.51, 2.53, 2.57.

4. Finally, try the SELF-TEST QUESTIONS and compare your solutions with those given.

# LEARNING OBJECTIVES

## A. CORRELATION

1. Compute the correlation coefficient $r$ for small sets of observations, using Equation 2.3 of the text.
2. Know the 4 basic properties of correlation that are listed following Example 2.17 in the text.

## B. CORRELATION AND REGRESSION

1. Use $r^2$ to describe the extent to which the variation in one variable can be accounted for by straight-line dependence on another variable.
2. Give the equation of the regression line of $y$ on $x$ from the means $\overline{x}$ and $\overline{y}$, the standard deviations $s_x$ and $s_y$, and the correlation coefficient $r$. Use Equation 2.4 to find the slope $b$ and the fact that $a = \overline{y} - b\overline{x}$ to find the intercept $a$.
3. Know that the regression line of $y$ on $x$ always passes through the point $(\overline{x}, \overline{y})$.

## C. LIMITATIONS OF CORRELATION AND REGRESSION

1. Understand that neither $r$ nor the least-squares regression line is resistant. Both can be strongly influenced by a few observations.
2. Understand that even a strong correlation does not mean that there is a cause-and-effect relationship between the two variables.

## SELF-TEST QUESTIONS

When adults are asked their weight, the weight that they report tends to be less than their actual weight as measured by a scale. But there is a strong relationship between reported weight and measured weight, because heavy people usually report higher weights than do light people. Here are the measured weights $x$ and reported weights $y$ (in pounds) for 5 female subjects.

| x | 112 | 123 | 178 | 141 | 135 |
|---|---|---|---|---|---|
| y | 110 | 120 | 165 | 125 | 129 |

**9.1** Make a scatterplot of these data. Which observation has the greatest influence on the position of the regression line and the value of the correlation coefficient?

**9.2** Compute the correlation coefficient $r$ between $x$ and $y$. What percent of the variation in the weights reported by these subjects is accounted for by the fact that reported weight varies linearly with measured weight?

**9.3** Suppose that all of the subjects reported a weight 5 pounds less than the values of $y$ in the table. Would this change the value of $r$?

**9.4** Use your value of the correlation $r$ and the means and standard deviations of $x$ and $y$ to give the equation of the least-squares regression line of reported weight on measured weight. Draw this line on your scatterplot.

**9.5** Explain what is wrong with each of the following statements.
(a) "Our study shows that the correlation between a voter's religion

and the political party he or she prefers is $r = 0.45$."
(b) "We found that the correlation between the number of hours per week a student spends watching television and the student's grades is $r = -1.13$."

## SELF-TEST SOLUTIONS

Figure 9.1

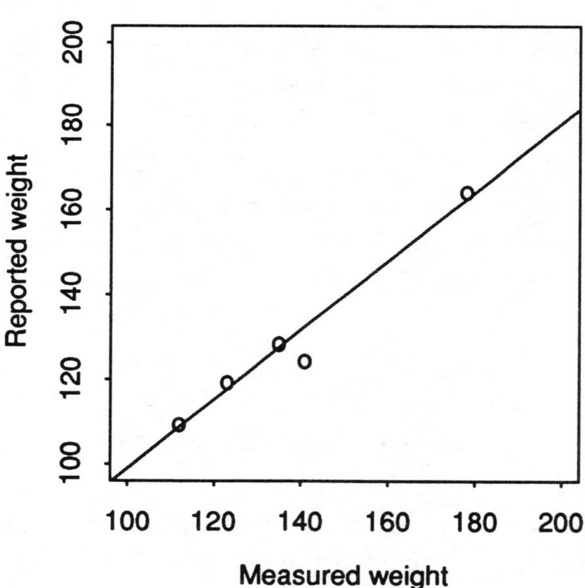


**9.1** The scatterplot appears in Figure 9.1. (Remember that when $x$ and $y$ have the same units it is good practice to use the same scales on both axes.) The observation with measured weight $x = 178$ pounds is most influential because it is an outlier in both the $x$ direction and the $y$ direction.

**9.2** To do the calculation with a basic calculator, follow the pattern of Example 2.17 in the text. First calculate the basic sums:

$$\begin{aligned}
\sum x &= 112 + \cdots + 135 = 689 \\
\sum x^2 &= (112)^2 + \cdots + (135)^2 = 97,463 \\
\sum y &= 110 + \cdots + 129 = 649 \\
\sum y^2 &= (110)^2 + \cdots + (129)^2 = 85,991 \\
\sum xy &= (112)(110) + \cdots + (135)(129) = 91,490
\end{aligned}$$

Second, calculate the means and standard deviations of both variables:

$$\begin{aligned}
\overline{x} &= \frac{1}{n}\sum x = \frac{689}{5} = 137.8 \\
\overline{y} &= \frac{1}{n}\sum y = \frac{649}{5} = 129.8 \\
s_x^2 &= \frac{1}{n-1}\{\sum x^2 - \frac{1}{n}(\sum x)^2\} \\
&= \frac{1}{4}\{97,463 - \frac{(689)^2}{5}\} \\
&= \frac{1}{4}\{97,463 - 94,944.2\} = 629.7 \\
s_x &= \sqrt{629.7} = 25.09 \\
s_y^2 &= \frac{1}{n-1}\{\sum y^2 - \frac{1}{n}(\sum y)^2\} \\
&= \frac{1}{4}\{85,991) - \frac{(649)^2}{5}\} \\
&= \frac{1}{4}\{85,991 - 84,240.2\} = 437.7 \\
s_y &= \sqrt{437.7} = 20.92
\end{aligned}$$

Finally, substitute into the computing formula Equation 2.3 for the correlation coefficient.

$$\begin{aligned} r &= \frac{\sum xy - \frac{1}{n}(\sum x)(\sum y)}{(n-1)s_x s_y} \\ &= \frac{91,490 - \frac{1}{5}(689)(649)}{(4)(25.09)(20.92)} \\ &= \frac{2057.8}{2099.53} = 0.980 \end{aligned}$$

If your calculator has statistical functions, find the means, standard deviations, and correlation coefficient using these functions. An exact calculation that carries many significant digits will give $r = .9799$.

The proportion of the variation in $y$ explained by linear dependence on $x$ is

$$r^2 = 0.98^2 = 0.96$$

or 96%. There is a very strong linear association between reported weight and measured weight.

**9.3** Subtracting 5 from each value of $y$ does not change the correlation $r$. (Notice that the correlation does not tell us how much the subjects understate their weight, only how strong the relation between reported and measured weight is.)

**9.4** First use Equation 2.4 to find the slope of the regression line:

$$\begin{aligned} b &= r\frac{s_y}{s_x} \\ &= .98\frac{20.92}{25.09} = 0.817 \end{aligned}$$

Then the intercept is

$$a = \overline{y} - b\overline{x}$$

$$= \quad 129.8 - (.817)(137.8) = 17.22$$

The least-squares regression line is therefore

$$\hat{y} = 17.22 + 0.817x$$

To plot this line on your scatterplot, choose two values of $x$, find the corresponding values of $\hat{y}$, mark these two points on the graph, and draw the straight line through them. For example, if $x = 120$ then

$$\hat{y} = 17.22 + (.817)(120) = 115.3$$

so (120,115.3) is one of the two points needed. The regression line also appears in Figure 9.1.

**9.5** (a) Both religion and political party are categorical variables. The correlation coefficient does not make sense for categorical variables; remember that $r$ measures only straight line association between two quantitative variables.
(b) The value of $r$ must lie between $-1$ and 1; an arithmetic error has been made in this case.

# UNIT 10
# MULTIDIMENSIONAL DATA ANALYSIS

## LESSON OVERVIEW

The video program for this unit completes the presentation of data analysis by showing the use of computing technology and by a case study that uses many of the tools you have learned to this point. The assignment for the unit is a review assignment, and the self-test is a sample examination that covers Units 2 to 9.

Data analysis in practice is carried out with the aid of **statistical software** on a computer. One function of software is to do calculations quickly and accurately. Another is to prepare graphs quickly for our inspection. Yet another is to store and manipulate data sets too large to be practical for analysis with a calculator. Modern computing facilities extend these basic functions in two important ways. First, they are **interactive**, so that the computer responds immediately to your command. This enables you to inspect the result and take the next step in the data analysis with better information. Second, statistical computing now features **graphical output** on a high-resolution screen. The text emphasizes the importance of graphing data; modern computing allows you to make more elaborate graphical displays immediately and to interact with them.

The video shows graphics for statistical analysis as practiced at Bell Communications Research. The first general principle illustrated is the effectiveness of human-machine interaction. The computer calculates and graphs very quickly, while the human eye and mind see patterns and draw conclusions in ways that are beyond the power of machines. This is why interactive graphics are so important in statistical computing. Some of the displays, such as scatterplots, are familiar to you. But now we can display several scatterplots when more than two variables are present, and can link points corresponding to the same cases on several plots. The software allows you to move a **brush**, a rectangle on the screen whose size and shape you can choose, over one scatterplot. The matching points on the other plots are automatically highlighted. This allows you to see relationships between more than two variables.

Brushing is one way the computer can help us grasp **multivariate data**, in which more than two variables are measured on each case. Earlier units showed statistical methods for a single variable (Units 2 to 5), for a variable changing over time (Units 6 and 7), and for relations between two variables (Units 8 and 9). A look a new computer-aided methods for inspecting many variables at once completes this development.

A computer screen, like a piece of paper, is two-dimensional. A scatterplot for two variables uses both dimensions. How can we display data with more than two dimensions? Several scatterplots display the variables two at a time, and brushing helps us see multivariate relations. Another method is to try to present a multivariate scatterplot directly.

A scatterplot of three variables, for example, is a cloud of points in space. To make the third dimension visible on a flat screen, computing systems use **color** or **motion**. Notice in the video how motion in particular makes a three-dimensional pattern apparent. Modern statistical software allows you to roam around a three-dimensional scatterplot until you find a viewpoint that reveals the nature of the relations. The video illustrates this by looking at the epicenters of earthquakes in the Fiji Islands, where the third dimension is depth beneath the earth. The proper viewpoint shows that the epicenters mark the boundaries between two moving plates on the earth's surface, whose collision causes the earthquakes. The same idea can be applied to data with four or more dimensions. A scatterplot of two of the variables is a particular two-dimensional view; it takes more experience to grasp changing two-dimensional views as the computer changes viewpoints.

Another way to present multivariate data on a flat screen or piece of paper is to use a representation unrelated to a scatterplots. Many such graphs have been invented. The video looks at one chosen because it is easy to understand: **faces**. Each variable controls one feature of a cartoon human face, so that different relations between the variables result in faces with different expressions. The human eye and mind can sometimes use the faces to group cases that are similar and to distinguish them from other cases. For example, very good forged currency has been distinguished from genuine currency by making several measurements and representing them as a face.

The video concludes with an example of a study that analyzes data on many variables to get a picture of environmental stresses in Chesapeake Bay. The variety and abundance of creatures living in the Bay's sediments, the level of salt and dissolved oxygen in the water, and other variables are measured at many locations over several years. Numerical and graphical tools for data analysis help turn this mass of numbers into conclusions about the effect of human activities on the Bay.

# ASSIGNMENT

1. Review the previously assigned sections of the text and your corrected assignments and self-tests on this material.

2. Do the following problems from the CHAPTER EXERCISES at the end of Chapters 1 and 2 in the text: 1.109, 1.112, 1.113, 2.92, 2.93, 2.97.

3. Work SAMPLE EXAMINATION 1 under examination conditions (that is, without referring to the text unless examinations in your course are open-book). Compare your answers with the solutions given, and review again any material that you had trouble with.

# SAMPLE EXAMINATION 1

## PART I–MULTIPLE CHOICE–2 POINTS EACH

**1** The histogram above displays the salaries of all 243 major league baseball players who batted at least 200 times in 1987, in thousands of dollars. This distribution is
(a) approximately symmetric
(b) symmetric except for a few outliers
(c) strongly skewed to the right
(d) strongly skewed to the left

**2** From the shape of the histogram above it is clear that the mean salary

of these baseball players
(a) is larger than the median salary
(b) is about the same as the median salary
(c) is smaller than the median salary
(d) can be either smaller or larger than the median salary—only a calculation can tell which

**3** The histogram above shows that the number of players who made between $400,000 and $600,000 in 1987 is about
(a) 59
(b) 49
(c) 40
(d) none of these

**4** The histogram is preferable to a stemplot for displaying the salaries of these baseball players because
(a) a stemplot for 243 observations would be cumbersome
(b) the histogram reports more detail than a stemplot does
(c) stemplots cannot be used when the observations are large numbers such as $400,000
(d) stemplots are only used to compare several distributions, not to display a single distribution

**5** You are writing an article on salaries in major league baseball based on the data displayed in the histogram above. You decide to report the median salary. To describe the variation or spread in salaries about the median, you might use
(a) the standard deviation
(b) the quartiles and extremes (smallest and largest salaries)
(c) the correlation coefficient
(c) the variance

**6** A study reports a correlation of $r = -0.71$ between family income in dollars and the number of pounds of soft margarine the family consumes in a year. You conclude that
(a) this is nonsense—you can't compute a correlation between income and amount of margarine
(b) something is wrong—a correlation can't take the value $-0.71$
(c) higher income families consume less soft margarine than do lower income families
(d) higher income families consume more soft margarine than do lower income families

**7** You are calculating the mean and standard deviation of 15 reaction times in a psychology experiment. Each reaction time is measured in seconds. Your results are $\overline{x} = 0.54$ and $s = -0.12$. You conclude that your arithmetic is wrong because
(a) the $\overline{x}$ value is impossible
(b) $s$ must always be larger than $\overline{x}$
(c) $s$ must always equal the square root of $\overline{x}$
(d) the $s$ value is impossible

**8** You are told that your score on an examination was at the 65th percentile. Your score was
(a) above the third quartile
(b) between the median and the third quartile
(c) between the first quartile and the median
(d) below the first quartile

**9** Scores on the American College Testing (ACT) college entrance examination have a distribution given approximately by this normal curve

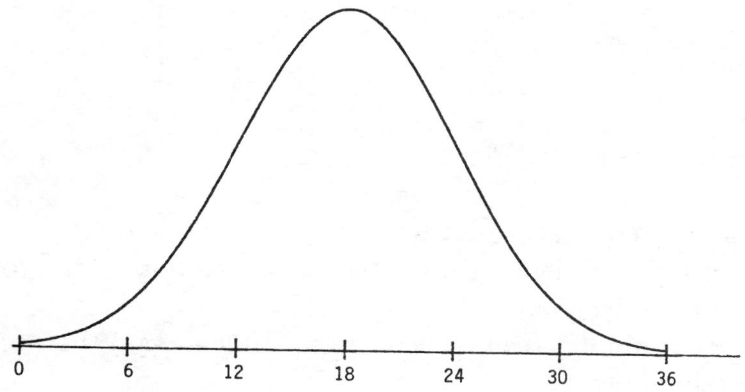


The mean of this distribution is
(a) 18
(b) 6
(c) 0 because the curve is symmetric
(d) can't tell from the curve

**10** The standard deviation of the distribution of ACT scores is
(a) 6
(b)12
(c)18
(d) can't tell from the curve

**11** The median ACT score in the distribution in Question 9 is
(a) greater than the mean
(b) equal to the mean
(c) less than the mean
(d) could be either greater or less than the mean

**12** 95% of all students who take the ACT test in Question 9 have scores between
(a) 0 and 36
(b) 6 and 30
(c) 12 and 24
(d) can't tell from the curve

**13** You would use a scatterplot to display
(a) the percent of students in a statistics course who come from each class (freshman to senior)
(b) the relationship between the sex of the students and their scores on a course examination
(c) the distribution of grade point average among all students enrolled in the course
(d) the relationship between grade point average of the students and their scores on a course examination

**14** The federal government collects data on the amount of retail sales (in dollars) each month. You expect retail sales to rise each December and fall each January because of the effect of Christmas buying. This kind of variation in time series data is called
(a) trend
(b) cycles
(c) seasonal variation
(d) erratic fluctuation

**15** A psychologist studies the effect of marital status on mental state. She finds that married women are more content with themselves on the average than are unmarried women. The explanatory variable in this study is
(a) marital status

(b) the women interviewed
(c) degree of self-contentment
(d) the psychologist

**16** Anthropologists must often estimate from human remains how tall the person was when alive. To do this we study how overall height can be predicted from the length of a leg bone in a group of 36 living males. The data show that the bone lengths have mean 45.9 centimeters and standard deviation 4.20 cm, overall height for the same men has mean 172.7 cm and standard deviation 8.14 cm, and the correlation between bone length and height is 0.914. The slope of the least-squares regression line of height on bone length is about
(a) 0.47
(b) 1.77
(c) 151.1
(d) 91.5
(d) none of these

**17** About what percent of the observed variation in the heights of the men studied in Question 16 is explained by the length of the leg bone?
(a) 91%
(b) 22%
(c) 3%
(d) 47%
(e) none of these

**18** You can best recognize whether or not a variable is growing exponentially over time by
(a) plotting the variable against time and looking for a straight-line pattern
(b) calculating the least-squares regression line of the variable against

time and examining the residuals
(c) plotting the logarithm of the variable against time and looking for a straight-line pattern
(d) smoothing the time series by running medians of three or five

**19** The running medians of three from the following data

23, 24, 21, 21, 29, 24, 24, 22

are
(a) 23, 23, 21, 21, 24, 24, 24, 22
(b) 23, 21, 21, 24, 24, 24
(c) 23, 23, 21, 21, 24, 24, 24, 24
(d) 23, 23, 21, 21, 24, 24, 22, 22

**20** An important overall strategy in examining data is
(a) don't trust graphs—do calculations instead
(b) look first for an overall pattern and then for important deviations from that pattern
(c) immediately discard any outlying or extreme observations
(d) always use means and standard deviations rather than other measures such as the five-number summary

## PART II

**1** (18 points) The table below gives the percent of the population in each of the 20 most populous states who live in metropolitan areas. (The government's official definition of "metropolitan area" is quite broad, including counties adjacent to and economically integrated with urban areas.)

| State | % Metro | State | % Metro |
|---|---|---|---|
| Massachusetts | 90.8 | New York | 90.5 |
| New Jersey | 100.0 | Penn. | 84.6 |
| Ohio | 78.8 | Indiana | 68.0 |
| Illinois | 82.4 | Michigan | 80.2 |
| Wisconsin | 66.5 | Missouri | 65.9 |
| Maryland | 92.9 | Virginia | 71.5 |
| N. Carolina | 55.0 | Georgia | 64.3 |
| Florida | 90.9 | Tennessee | 66.8 |
| Louisiana | 69.1 | Texas | 80.7 |
| Washington | 81.0 | California | 95.7 |

Make a stemplot to display the distribution, and give the five-number summary. Are there any outliers or other unusual features?

**2** (18 points) The length of human pregnancies from conception to birth varies according to a distribution that is approximately normal with mean 266 days and standard deviation 16 days.
(a) Julie starts a new job on September 1 and has a baby the following May 31, 272 days later. The company refuses to cover the delivery costs under its medical insurance program on the grounds that the pregnancy was a "preexisting condition" because the baby was born less than 9 months after employment began. What percent of all pregnancies last 272 days or less?
(b) How long do the longest 1% of human pregnancies last?

**3** (24 points) Chemical theory predicts that over a restricted range of time the yield of a chemical reaction used in producing a pharmaceutical product will increase linearly with the time that the reaction is allowed to continue. Here are data from an experiment with this process conducted by the engineer in charge. Reaction time is measured in minutes and yield in percent of the desired product in the output of the reaction. A scatterplot of the data appears below. Notice that the engineer ran the reaction twice for each length of time; the first five runs were done on one day and the next five on the following day.

| Time | 10 | 11 | 12 | 13 | 14 | 10 | 11 | 12 | 13 | 14 |
|---|---|---|---|---|---|---|---|---|---|---|
| Yield | 16.5 | 18.0 | 19.9 | 20.4 | 22.1 | 18.7 | 20.7 | 20.2 | 21.8 | 22.4 |

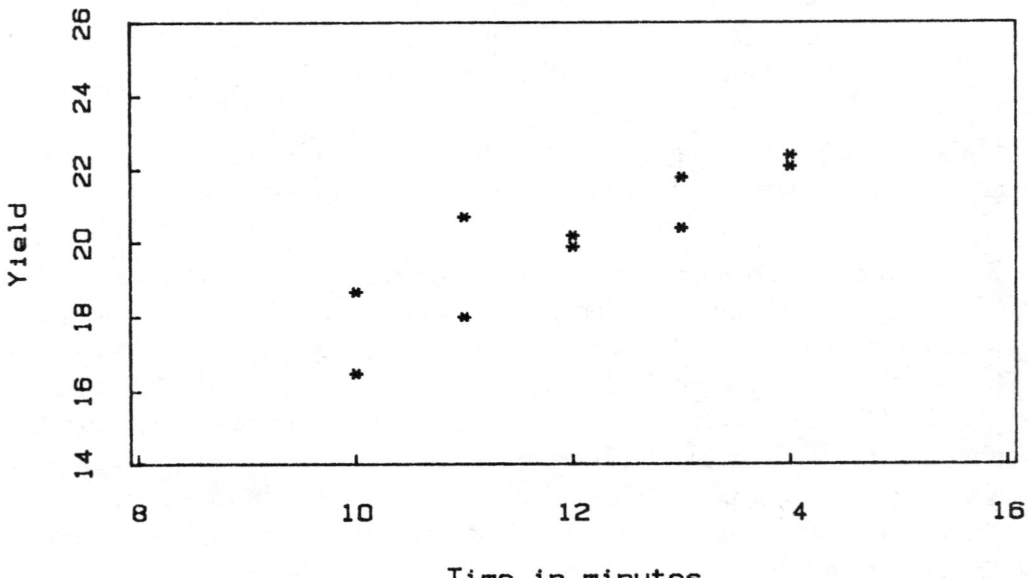


(a) Is the pattern roughly linear? In particular, do you think that a reaction time longer than 14 minutes should be tried to see if yield continues to increase? Are there any outliers?
(b) A computer least-squares routine tells you that the least-squares regression line of yield $y$ on time $t$ is

$$\hat{y} = 6.81 + 1.105t$$

By how much does the yield increase for every additional minute of time in this range of times?
(c) The regression line claims that the yield would be 6.81% when the reaction is run for no time at all ($t = 0$). The engineer knows that there would be no yield if $t = 0$. Explain why the regression line gives an incorrect result.
(d) Predict the yield if the process runs for 11 minutes.
(e) There are two residuals for $t = 11$. What are their values?
(f) A look at the data shows that the first yield for each reaction time has a negative residual, while the second has a positive residual. What do you suspect based on this pattern?

# SAMPLE EXAMINATION 1 SOLUTIONS

## PART I ANSWERS

**1** (c) A distribution with a right tail (high incomes in this case) extending farther from the bulk of the data than does the left tail is called skewed to the right.

**2** (a) The mean is not resistant, so it moves toward the long tail of a skewed distribution farther than the median does.

**3** (c) The bases of the bars cover 0–200, 200–400, 400–600, and so on. The count (frequency) in the $400,000 to $600,000 class is the height of the third bar from the left, which is about 40.

**4** (a) In general, stemplots are better for smaller sets of data and histograms for larger sets. Notice that to use a stemplot for large values like $400,000 you would truncate the observation to 400 or to 40.

**5** (b) The standard deviation and variance measure spread about the mean and so should not be used with the median. The correlation does not measure spread.

**6** (c) The negative value of $r$ indicates a negative association between income and soft margarine consumption: as income goes up, margarine consumed tends to go down.

**7** (d) $s$ must always be 0 or positive

**8** (b) The median is the 50th percentile (that is, 50 percent of the scores fall below it) and the third quartile is the 75th percentile. The 65th percentile lies between these two points.

**9** (a) The mean lies at the center of symmetry.

**10** (a) The standard deviation is the distance from the mean (18) to the change of curvature points (12 and 24) on either side.

**11** (b) The median and the mean are equal in any symmetric distribution.

**12** (b) The 68–95–99.7 rule says that in any normal distribution 95% of the observations fall within two standard deviations on either side of the mean.

**13** (d) A scatterplot displays the relationship between two quantitative variables.

**14** (c) Regular movements that recur each year are seasonal variation.

**15** (a) Degree of contentment is the response variable.

**16** (b) The slope is found from Equation (3.5) in the text.

$$\begin{aligned} b &= r\frac{s_y}{s_x} \\ &= .914 \times \frac{8.14}{4.20} = 1.77 \end{aligned}$$

It is important to recognize that we want to predict height from bone length, so that bone length is the explanatory variable $x$.

**17** (e) The "percentage of variation explained" by the linear relationship between $x$ and $y$ is $r^2 = .914^2 = .835$, or about 83%.

**18** (c) The logarithm of a variable that grows exponentially over time grows linearly.

**19** (a) Replace each value except the first and last with the median of that value and those next to it on either side. The first and last values in the series are left unchanged because they do not have entries both above and below them.

**20** (b)

## PART II ANSWERS

**1** To make a stemplot, truncate the observations to two digits and use the first (10s digit) as the stem. If you prefer to round rather than truncate, that is also acceptable. With 20 observations on six stems, it is better not to split the stems. Here is the stemplot:

| | |
|---|---|
| 5 | 5 |
| 6 | 456689 |
| 7 | 18 |
| 8 | 00124 |
| 9 | 00025 |
| 10 | 0 |

There are no clear outliers. The distribution shows some signs of having two peaks but does not display any really striking features such as skewness.

To give the five-number summary, use the stemplot to arrange the observations in increasing order. (The actual data appear here; it is acceptable to use the truncated values from the stemplot to speed your work.)

| | | | | | | | | | |
|---|---|---|---|---|---|---|---|---|---|
| 55.0 | 64.3 | 65.9 | 66.5 | 66.8 | 68.0 | 69.1 | 71.5 | 78.8 | 80.2 |
| 80.7 | 81.0 | 82.4 | 84.6 | 90.5 | 90.8 | 90.9 | 92.9 | 95.7 | 100.0 |

Because $n = 20$, the median has position $(n + 1)/2 = 10.5$ in the list, or midway between the 10th and 11th entries. So

$$M = \frac{80.2 + 80.7}{2} = 80.45$$

The first quartile is the median of the 10 observations below 80.45, and the third quartile is the median of the 10 observations above this value. So

$$\begin{aligned} Q_1 &= \frac{66.8 + 68.0}{2} = 67.4 \\ Q_2 &= \frac{90.5 + 90.8}{2} = 90.65 \end{aligned}$$

The five-number summary is therefore

$$55.0 \quad 67.4 \quad 80.45 \quad 90.65 \quad 100.0$$

**2** (a) The length $X$ of a pregnancy has the $N(266, 16)$ distribution. So the relative frequency of

$$X \leq 272$$

is found by first standardizing

$$\begin{aligned} \frac{X - 266}{16} &\leq \frac{272 - 266}{16} \\ Z &\leq .375 \end{aligned}$$

and then finding from Table A in the text that the area to the left of 0.38 under the standard normal curve is 0.6480 or about 65%. The company's policy is not reasonable.
(b) We must find the length $L$ such that the relative frequency of $X \geq L$ is 0.01. That is, the relative frequency of $X < L$ is 0.99. Standardizing, this event is

$$\begin{aligned} \frac{X - 266}{16} &< \frac{L - 266}{16} \\ Z &< \frac{L - 266}{16} \end{aligned}$$

From Table A, the entry closest to .99 is .9901, the entry for $z = 2.33$. So

$$\frac{L - 266}{16} = 2.33$$

and solving this equation for $L$ gives

$$L = 266 + (16)(2.33) = 303.3$$

That is, the longest 1% of pregnancies last 303 days or longer.

**3** (a) The pattern is quite linear. Because the linear trend is still present at $t = 14$ minutes, it is reasonable to try the experiment with longer reaction times to obtain higher yields. There are no outliers.
(b) The slope of the fitted line is $b = 1.105$, so on the average the yield increases by 1.105% for each additional minute of reaction time.
(c) The relation between reaction time and yield is linear for times between 10 minutes and 14 minutes. It may not be linear outside that range; in particular, the relation cannot be linear all the way down to $t = 0$. Using the intercept of the fitted line to predict the yield at time $t = 0$ is an example of extrapolation.
(d) The predicted yield at time $t = 11$ is

$$\begin{aligned} \hat{y} &= 6.81 + 1.105t \\ &= 6.81 + (1.105)(11) = 18.965\% \end{aligned}$$

(e) The two observed yields for reaction times of 11 minutes were 18.0% and 20.7%. The residuals for these two observations are

$$\begin{aligned} \text{residual} &= \text{observed} - \text{predicted} \\ &= 18.0 - 18.965 = -0.965 \quad \text{and} \\ &= 20.7 - 18.965 = 1.735 \end{aligned}$$

(f) The first run at each reaction time was made on one day and the second run on a different day. The fact that all observations from the first day have negative residuals and all those from the second day have positive residuals suggests that something changed between days that raised the yields on the second day. The engineer should attempt to discover how conditions changed from day to day.

# UNIT 11
# THE QUESTION OF CAUSATION

## LESSON OVERVIEW

This unit is centered on the very important fact that a statistical association between two variables need not indicate that there is a cause and effect relationship between the variables. Because the different kinds of relationships that may account for an observed association between two variables are clearest for categorical variables, the unit begins by describing association between categorical variables.

The relationship between two categorical variables is described by a **two-way table** of counts or percents. Two-way tables are often used to summarize large amounts of data by grouping outcomes into categories. A two-way table allows us to calculate the **marginal distribution** of each variable alone from the row sums and column sums. We can also obtain the **conditional distribution** of one variable given a specific level of the other by considering table entries as proportions of their row or column sums. A **segmented bar graph** visually compares a set of conditional distributions. Relationships among three categorical variables are described by a **three-way table**, which is printed as separate two-way tables for each level of the third variable.

Three-way tables allow us to see how a third variable (a **lurking variable**) can influence the association between two variables. A comparison between two variables that holds for each level of a third variable can be changed or even reversed when the data are aggregated by summing over all levels of the third variable. **Simpson's paradox** refers to the reversal of a comparison by aggregation. In the video, Simpson's paradox is illustrated by admissions data at a fictional university: Business and Law each admit a higher percent of female applicants than of male applicants, but the two professional schools together admit a higher percent of male applicants than of female applicants. So an apparent preference for men in the overall data turns into a preference for women in each school individually.

An observed association between two variables can be due to any of **causation**, **common response**, or **confounding**. Both common response and confounding involve the effect of other variables on the response. That an association is due to causation is best established by an **experiment** in which the explanatory variable is directly changed and other influences on the response are controlled. In the absence of experimental evidence, causation should be only cautiously accepted. Good evidence of causation requires that the association be observed in many varied studies, that examination of the effects of other variables not remove the association, and that a clear explanation for the alleged causation exist. As an example of the way in which evidence for causation is gathered when experiments cannot be done, the video presents a historical documentary on smoking and lung cancer. It is now accepted that smoking is a cause of lung cancer, but reaching this conclusion took many years.

## ASSIGNMENT

1. Read the LEARNING OBJECTIVES to see what specific skills you must acquire from this unit.

2. Read Sections 2.5 and 2.6 of the text.

3. Do the following problems from the SECTION 2.5 EXERCISES in the text: 2.69, 2.71, 2.77; also do the following problems from the SECTION 2.6 EXERCISES: 2.83, 2.87.

4. Finally, try the SELF-TEST QUESTIONS and compare your answers with those given.

## LEARNING OBJECTIVES

A. Arrange information about two categorical variables in a two-way table and describe the association between the variables by calculating and comparing appropriate percents.

B. Calculate from a two-way table the marginal distribution of each variable and the conditional distribution of one variable given a specific value of the other variable.

C. Arrange information about three categorical variables in a three-way table, and from this table obtain the two-way table for any two of the variables.

D. Recognize Simpson's paradox in three-way categorical data, and use the data to explain how the paradox arises.

E. Recognize possible instances of common response or confounding when examining the association between two variables.

F. Recognize the quality of evidence for causation, from experiments or from the combination of many non-experimental studies.

## SELF-TEST QUESTIONS

**11.1** The following three-way table classifies the U.S. male labor force in 1989 by age, race, and employment status. Table entries are in thousands of men. (For simplicity, only white and black men are included.)

| | WHITE | | BLACK | |
|---|---|---|---|---|
| Age | Employed | Not | Employed | Not |
| 16–19 | 3060 | 487 | 327 | 153 |
| 20–34 | 22,222 | 1170 | 2673 | 388 |
| 35–64 | 29,272 | 941 | 2799 | 221 |
| $\geq 65$ | 1797 | 38 | 131 | 10 |
| Total | 56,351 | 2636 | 5930 | 772 |

(a) From this three-way table, obtain the two-way table that classifies the male labor force by age and employment.
(b) Describe the association between age and unemployment, using appropriate percents in your description.

(c) Give (in percents) the marginal distribution of the age of male workers.
(d) Give the distribution of the age of unemployed workers. (This is the conditional distribution of workers' age given that they are unemployed.)

**11.2** The following three-way table gives data on unemployment in a small community. Show that Simpson's paradox holds: in each age group the percent of whites who are unemployed is greater than the percent of unemployed blacks, but overall the percent of blacks who are unemployed is higher. Then explain clearly why the paradox occurs in this particular case.

| | WHITE | | BLACK | |
|---|---|---|---|---|
| Age | Employed | Not | Employed | Not |
| $\leq 25$ | 200 | 100 | 500 | 200 |
| $> 25$ | 950 | 50 | 450 | 20 |
| Total | 1150 | 150 | 950 | 220 |

**11.3** An article in a women's magazine notes that mothers who nurse their infants have (on the average) more positive feelings toward their babies than mothers who bottle-feed their infants. The author concludes that nursing causes the mother to feel closer to the child. Explain how nursing or not nursing is confounded with the attitude toward the child that the mother already has, so that the cause and effect conclusion is not justified.

**11.4** Does driving with the car's headlights on during the day reduce traffic accidents? Explain why data showing that drivers who leave their lights on do have fewer accidents is not good evidence that turning on the lights causes fewer accidents. Then suggest briefly what kind of evidence you would find more convincing.

## SELF-TEST SOLUTIONS

**11.1** (a) To obtain the two-way table, add the "BLACK" and "WHITE" entries in the three-way table. For example, the number aged 16–19 and unemployed is $487 + 153 = 640$. The row totals are needed in (b) and (c), so they are added to the two-way table:

| Age | Employed | Not employed | Total |
|---|---|---|---|
| 16–19 | 3387 | 640 | 4027 |
| 20–34 | 24,895 | 1558 | 26,453 |
| 35–64 | 32,071 | 1162 | 33,233 |
| $\geq 65$ | 1928 | 48 | 1976 |
| Total | 62,281 | 3408 | 65,689 |

(b) The association between age and unemployment is best described by comparing the percent of unemployed workers in each age group. This is the "Not employed" entry in each row as a percent of the row total. For example, the percent unemployed in the 16–19 age group is

$$\frac{640}{4027} = 0.159 = 15.9\%$$

The percent unemployed is 5.9% for 20–34 year-olds, 3.5% for 35–64 year-olds, and 2.4% for men over 65. There is a strong *negative association* between unemployment and age, with younger workers suffering much higher unemployment than older workers.

(c) The marginal distribution of age appears in the right ("Total") column of the table. To give the distribution in percent, give each row total as a percent of the table total. For example, the percent of workers who are 16 to 19 years old is

$$\frac{4027}{65,689} = 0.061 = 6.1\%$$

The entire marginal distribution is:

| Age | 16–19 | 20–34 | 35–64 | $\geq 65$ |
|---|---|---|---|---|
| % | 6.1 | 40.3 | 50.6 | 3.0 |

(d) The conditional distribution of age among unemployed workers looks only at the "Not employed" column and gives each entry as a percent of the column total. For example, the percent of the unemployed who are 16 to 19 is

$$\frac{640}{378} = 0.188 = 18.8\%$$

The entire conditional distribution is

| Age | 16–19 | 20–34 | 35–64 | $\geq 65$ |
|---|---|---|---|---|
| % | 18.8 | 45.7 | 34.1 | 1.4 |

Comparing this distribution with the distribution of the ages of all male workers in (c) shows again that unemployed workers tend to be younger than the labor force as a whole.

**11.2** For young workers (25 or younger) the white unemployment rate is 100/300, or 33%. The black percent unemployed is 200/700, or 28.6%. So a higher percent of young whites are unemployed. The percent unemployed among older white workers is 50/1000, or 5%. For older black workers the result is 20/470, or 4.3%. Once again the white percent unemployed is higher.

Now combine the two age groups and look at all white workers. There are 1300 whites in all, of whom 150 are not employed. That's 150/3000 or 5% unemployed. There are 1170 black workers in the community, of whom 220 are not employed. The black unemployment rate is 220/1170, or 18.8%. The black unemployment rate is much higher than the white rate, even though the white rate is higher in each of the two age groups separately. That's Simpson's paradox.

The explanation in this case is that young workers are much more likely to be unemployed than older workers, and in this community more than half of the black workers but less than one-fourth of the white workers are young. The unusual concentration of black workers in the younger age group accounts for the paradox.

**11.3** Mothers choose whether or not to nurse their infants. It may be that women who already feel positively about the baby choose to nurse, while those to whom the child is a nuisance choose the bottle. So when we look at the mother's attitude sometime later, the effect of nursing or not is confounded with the effect of the mother's earlier attitude.

**11.4** As long as drivers choose whether or not to keep their lights on, it may be that cautious drivers (who would have fewer accidents anyway) choose to drive with their lights on. Accidents and lights-on driving may be a common response to the overall caution of the driver.

The strongest evidence for causation would be provided by an *experiment* in which some drivers are told to keep their lights on and others are told to keep lights off during daylight. Keep track of the accident rate in the two groups to see if the lights-on group has fewer accidents. In the absence of an experiment, we would like data on drivers on many different types (such as different ages and in several countries). If those who drive with their lights on always have fewer accidents, the conclusion is strengthened a bit even though common response is still present. Notice that there is a plausible reason why driving with lights on could reduce accidents: it makes your car more visible to other drivers.

# UNIT 12
# EXPERIMENTAL DESIGN

## LESSON OVERVIEW

The statistical techniques that you met in the first 10 units of this course enable you to explore and understand data. But when you want to answer a specific question, you need data that speak to that question. **Anecdotal evidence** based on a few individual cases is rarely trustworthy. **Available data** collected for other purposes, such as census data, are often helpful. But sometimes we need to produce data of our own. Data intended to answer specific questions are usually produced by sampling or experimentation.

**Sampling** selects a part of a population of interest to represent the whole. **Experiments** are distinguished from observational studies by the fact that an experiment actually does something to the subjects of the experiment. Unit 11 pointed out that evidence for a direct effect of an explanatory variable on a response variable is best obtained from an experiment. The statistical principles used to design experiments are the topic of this unit. The video illustrates the distinction between observational studies and experiments by looking at research on the behavior of lobsters. Some studies carefully observe lobsters without doing anything to them. An experiment does something, such as add food coloring to the water to see if the lobster becomes disoriented when it cannot see.

In an experiment, one or more **treatments** are imposed on the experimental **units** or **subjects**. Each treatment is a combination of levels of the explanatory variables, which are often called **factors**. The experiments in this unit have only one factor. The **design** of an experiment refers to the choice of treatments and the manner in which the experimental units or subjects are assigned to the treatments. The video discusses the Physicians' Health Study, an important medical experiment that showed that taking aspirin regularly can reduce heart attacks. The subjects were 22,000 physicians; the treatments were aspirin tablets or a placebo (a dummy medicine) taken regularly. In this experiment, the explanatory variable (factor) is the type of medicine taken. The most important response variable is whether or not the subject suffers a heart attack.

There are three basic principles of statistical design of experiments. The first is **control**, which in its simplest form says that an experiment should compare several treatments. Experiments should be comparative in order to avoid **confounding** of the treatments with other influences, such as environmental variables. The second principle is **randomization**. Random assignment of the experimental units or subjects to the treatments creates treatment groups that are similar (except for chance variation) before the treatments are applied. Randomization and comparison together prevent **bias**, or systematic favoritism, in experiments. You will learn to carry out randomization by giving numerical labels to the experimental units and using a **table of random digits** to choose treatment groups. The third principle is **replication** of the treatments on many units. This reduces the role of chance variation and makes the experiment more sensitive to differences among the treatments.

In addition to the Physicians' Health Study, the video program describes an experiment that compares three treatments of domestic violence offenders: arrest and hold, arrest and release after booking, and mediation without an arrest. This story shows how randomized comparative experiments can help develop effective social policy.

The stories in this unit raise the issue of the ethics of using people as experimental subjects. Not all statisticians agree on the proper standards here, and these standards differ widely among fields in which statistics is applied. The stories contrast two different fields. Medical experiments are tightly regulated. Dr. Hennekens, director of the Physicians' Health Study, describes the delicate balance that justifies a medical experiment: enough knowledge to hope that a treatment will be helpful, but not enough knowledge to be sure. A good experiment can provide the missing information and save lives. Subjects in a medical experiment must give their informed consent to participate before they enter the experiment.

The domestic violence experiment is quite different. The subjects are not asked to give consent—but they become subjects by committing acts that justify their arrest. Insisting on the informed consent that is required in medical experiments would make the domestic violence experiment impossible. Although it seems arbitrary to decide the fate of a violent person at random, experiments like this changed police procedures across the country by showing that arresting offenders does reduce future violence. Only a randomized comparative experiment can give such strong evidence. A central ethical issue about experiments is balancing the rights of the subjects against the value (often to other people in the future) of the knowledge gained.

## ASSIGNMENT

1. Read the LEARNING OBJECTIVES to see what specific skills you must acquire from this unit.

2. Read Section 3.1 of the text and the part of Section 3.2 up to the heading "Other Experimental Designs."

3. Do the following problems from the SECTION 3.1 EXERCISES in the text: 3.3, 3.4; and the following problems from the SECTION 3.2 EXERCISES: 3.9, 3.13, 3.19, and 3.23.

4. Finally, try the SELF-TEST QUESTIONS and compare your answers with those given.

## LEARNING OBJECTIVES

A. Recognize whether or not a study is an experiment; identify the treatments, response variables, and experimental units or subjects in an experiment with a single factor.

B. Outline the design of a single-factor completely randomized experiment using a diagram like (3.3) in the text. The diagram in a specific case should include the sizes of the groups, the specific treatments, and the response variable as in Example 3.9.

C. Use Table B of random digits to carry out the random assignment of subjects to groups in a completely randomized experiment.

D. Recognize the placebo effect and the double-blind technique.

## SELF-TEST QUESTIONS

**12.1** An English teacher encourages students to use a word processing program on the school's computers to compose and revise their papers. There are two word processing programs available, UWRITE and DOWNWRITE. The computer keeps track of the time spent by each student. The teacher studies the data and sees that the students who use UWRITE spend 20% less time writing their papers than the students who use DOWNWRITE. Is this study an experiment? Explain why or why not.

**12.2** The teacher decides to carry out an experiment to determine which word processing program is faster for students to learn and use. The subjects will be the 32 students in next semester's course, none of whom have used either program before. The response variable will be the time required to prepare the first draft of a 5,000 word paper. Outline the design of a completely randomized experiment for the teacher to use.

**12.3** The following class list gives the names of the 32 students. Use Table B beginning at line 120 to carry out the random assignment required by your design in Question 12.2.

| | | | |
|---|---|---|---|
| Anderson | Evans | Jiang | Raab |
| Biehn | Finney | Jones | Reilly |
| Brinkman | Foster | Kamin | Scaletta |
| Calderone | Gallucci | Kim | Sego |
| Clark | Gobel | LaPlante | Ting |
| Dale | Hafen | Metcalf | Vasquez |
| DeLos | Hernandez | Moss | Vaughn |
| Everett | Hockema | Palmer | Young |

## SELF-TEST SOLUTIONS

**12.1** The students choose which word processing program to use. The study is not an experiment because no treatment is imposed on the students. It is an observational study.

**12.2** We will assign students to use a particular program at random and require them to use only that program. The two treatments to be compared are the two programs. In the absence of any reason to do otherwise, assign an equal number of students to each group. An outline of the design appears on the next page.

Notice that the diagram shows all of the essential elements of the design: the randomization, the sizes of the two groups, the two treatments, and the response variable.

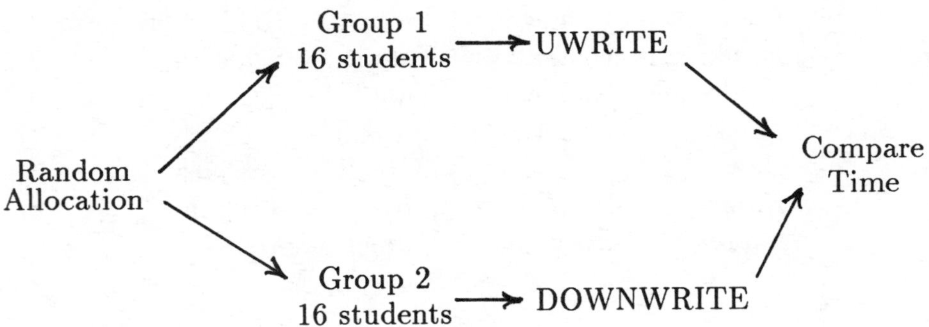


**12.3** First assign a numerical label to each student. Because there are 32 students, two-digit labels are needed. You can use either 00–31 or, as here, 01–32:

| | | | | | | | |
|---|---|---|---|---|---|---|---|
| 01 | Anderson | 09 | Evans | 17 | Jiang | 25 | Raab |
| 02 | Biehn | 10 | Finney | 18 | Jones | 26 | Reilly |
| 03 | Brinkman | 11 | Foster | 19 | Kamin | 27 | Scaletta |
| 04 | Calderone | 12 | Gallucci | 20 | Kim | 28 | Sego |
| 05 | Clark | 13 | Gobel | 21 | LaPlante | 29 | Ting |
| 06 | Dale | 14 | Hafen | 22 | Metcalf | 30 | Vasquez |
| 07 | DeLos | 15 | Hernandez | 23 | Moss | 31 | Vaughn |
| 08 | Everett | 16 | Hockema | 24 | Palmer | 32 | Young |

Now read two-digit groups from Table B, beginning at line 120 and continuing from line to line until 16 students are chosen. Ignore all groups that are not between 01 and 32, and also ignore any repeated groups. The 16 chosen form the first group, and the 16 remaining students make up the second group. The 16 chosen are:

16, 04, 26, 21, 19, 29, 07, 22, 10, 25, 13, 15, 05, 09, 08, 27

Circle these names in the list to see the randomly selected students more clearly.

# UNIT 13
# BLOCKING AND SAMPLING

## LESSON OVERVIEW

This unit has two main purposes. First, we look at some more complex designs for experiments, especially the use of blocking. **Blocks** are groups of experimental units or subjects that are similar in some way important to the response. In a randomized block design, randomization is carried out separately within each block. Forming blocks is another type of control in an experiment. The video shows an agricultural experiment in which the experimental units are small plots of land and the treatments are different varieties of strawberries. Because land in different locations varies in fertility, drainage, and other ways that affect plant growth, it is helpful to divide the land into blocks containing a few plots in the same location. The different varieties are then assigned at random to plots separately within each block. In addition to blocking, the unit also mentions experiments with more than one factor. In such experiments, a treatment consists of a particular value of each factor.

The second purpose of this unit is to introduce the design of sample surveys. In a sample survey, a **sample** is selected from the **population** of all people or things about which we desire information. Conclusions about the population are based on examination of the sample. The video program contrasts a sample with a **census** which attempts to examine every member of the population. Even a census is not completely accurate, as a discussion of the U.S. census shows. Some people are missed by the census, and this undercount is concentrated in the minority neighborhoods of large cities. Only a census can give detailed information about every part of a population, but for overall information a sample is usually faster, less expensive, and just as accurate. The varied uses of sampling are shown by a look at the manufacture of potato chips: sampling is used at every stage, from the arrival of potatoes at the plant to checking the final product on supermarket shelves.

The **design** of a sample refers to the method used to select the sample from the population. The most important statistical principle in sampling design is to select the sample at random from the population. The basic probability sample is a **simple random sample**, which gives every possible sample of a given size the same chance to be the sample selected. Simple random samples are chosen by labeling the members of the population and using random digits to select the sample. Random sampling avoids the systematic favoritism or **bias** that often results when a sample is formed by human choice.

## ASSIGNMENT

1. Read the LEARNING OBJECTIVES to see what specific skills you must acquire from this unit.

2. Read Section 3.2 of the text and Section 3.3 as far as the heading

"Other Sampling Designs."

3. Do the following problem from the SECTION 3.2 EXERCISES in the text: 3.26; and the following problems from the SECTION 3.3 EXERCISES: 3.29, 3.31, 3.35.

4. Finally, try the SELF-TEST QUESTIONS and compare your answers with those given.

## LEARNING OBJECTIVES

A. Identify the factors and treatments in a several-factor experiment; outline a completely randomized design with several factors.

B. Recognize when use of blocks is appropriate in an experimental design; outline a randomized block design with a single factor and use Table B to carry out the randomization.

C. Identify the population in a sampling situation; understand the distinction between a census and a sample.

D. Recognize the bias in voluntary response samples and other inferior sampling methods.

E. Use Table B of random digits to select a simple random sample (SRS) from a small population.

## SELF-TEST QUESTIONS

**13.1** A food scientist is interested in determining how the conditions under which soybeans are stored affect the "cookability" of the beans when they are processed. She will store lots of beans at each of 3 temperatures and 2 humidity levels for 2, 8, and 16 weeks, then process the beans and measure their cookability.

How many factors does this experiment have? Identify the factors and state how many levels each factor has. If all combinations are compared, how many different treatments are there in the experiment? What are the experimental units? What is the response variable?

**13.2** A medical experiment will compare a new medication intended to reduce high blood pressure with a standard medication. The subjects are 200 men aged 40 to 60 with high blood pressure in Minneapolis and another 300 similar men in San Francisco. Outline a randomized block design for this experiment.

**13.3** A member of Congress wants to know what the voters in his district think about a proposed gun control law. A staff member reports that 87 letters have been received on this subject, of which 73 oppose the law. That is, 84% of the letter-writers oppose gun control legislation.

What is the population in this problem? (Be as specific as possible.) The 87 letters are a sample. Explain why the sample result is almost certainly biased. Is the proportion of the population that oppose the proposed law probably greater or less than 84%?

**13.4** A student wants to study the responses that students receive when calling an academic department for information. She selects an SRS of 6 departments from the following list for her study. Use Table B starting at line 125 to choose the SRS.

| | | |
|---|---|---|
| Agronomy | Education | Nursing |
| Animal Science | Electrical Eng | Pharmacology |
| Audiology | English | Philosophy |
| Biochemistry | Foreign Languages | Physical Education |
| Biology | History | Physics |
| Chemistry | Horticulture | Political Science |
| Communication | Industrial Eng | Psychology |
| Computer Science | Mathematics | Sociology |
| Creative Arts | Mechanical Eng | Statistics |

## SELF-TEST SOLUTIONS

**13.1** There are 3 factors: temperature with 3 levels, humidity with 2 levels, and storage time with 3 levels. A treatment combines a particular temperature, humidity, and storage time. Each temperature can be combined with each humidity and each storage time, so in all there are $3 \times 2 \times 3 = 18$ possible treatments. The experimental units are the lots of soybeans that will be stored under experimental conditions and then processed. The response variable is the cookability of the beans. (A completely randomized design to compare all 18 treatments would have the familiar outline (3.3) of the text, but with 18 groups rather than two groups.)

**13.2** The men form two natural blocks: those in Minneapolis and those in San Francisco. Medical experiments are often carried out in several different locations, in which case each location is a block. The subjects in each block are separately assigned at random to the new or the standard medication. In Minneapolis, 100 subjects are assigned to each treatment; 150 men get each treatment in San Francisco. At the end of the experiment, the change in blood pressure is recorded. The outline is similar to Figure 3.2 in the text, though with 2 rather than 3 treatments compared in each block.

**13.3** There is no one correct answer for the population, since we cannot ask the congressman what group he wants information about. A good choice is all registered voters in his congressional district. Another possibility is all residents 18 years and older in his congressional district. Be sure to specify a population exactly, so that you can tell whether any person is or is not in the population.

Letters to a legislator are a form of voluntary response. Only people who feel strongly about an issue take the trouble to write, and their opinions may differ from those of the entire population. In the case of gun control, those opposed to gun control feel very strongly and are likely to write. So the sample is biased in the direction of overrepresenting opponents of gun control. The percent of the population who oppose the new law is certainly less than 84%.

**13.4** Label the population of 27 academic departments using two-digit labels.

| | | | | | |
|---|---|---|---|---|---|
| 01 | Agronomy | 10 | Education | 19 | Nursing |
| 02 | Animal Science | 11 | Electrical Eng | 20 | Pharmacology |
| 03 | Audiology | 12 | English | 21 | Philosophy |
| 04 | Biochemistry | 13 | Foreign Languages | 22 | Physical Education |
| 05 | Biology | 14 | History | 23 | Physics |
| 06 | Chemistry | 15 | Horticulture | 24 | Political Science |
| 07 | Communication | 16 | Industrial Eng | 25 | Psychology |
| 08 | Computer Science | 17 | Mathematics | 26 | Sociology |
| 09 | Creative Arts | 18 | Mechanical Eng | 27 | Statistics |

Now read two-digit groups from lines 125 and 126 of Table B until 6 departments are selected. The SRS consists of

| | |
|---|---|
| 21 | Philosophy |
| 18 | Mechanical Engineering |
| 23 | Physics |
| 19 | Nursing |
| 10 | Education |
| 08 | Computer Science |

# UNIT 14
# SAMPLES AND SURVEYS

## LESSON OVERVIEW

Although simple random samples are the foundation of sampling designs, sample surveys in practice usually use more complex designs. This unit begins with a look at these designs. In **stratified random sampling** the population is divided into **strata**, groups of units that are similar in some way important to the response. A separate SRS is then selected from each stratum. Stratified sampling designs are the analog of block designs for an experiment. The video program illustrates stratified sampling by a survey of recreational fisherman carried out by the National Marine Fisheries Service. The strata in this case are different locations for fishing.

National samples are usually **multistage samples** that select successively smaller regions within the population in stages. Each stage may employ an SRS, a stratified sample, or another type of sample. The General Social Survey conducted by the National Opinion Research Center is an example of a national sample that provides important information about public sentiment.

Failure to use probability sampling often results in **bias**, or systematic errors in the way the sample represents the population. This unit also reminds us of some of the practical difficulties that may cause bias when sampling people. A sampling design that systematically misses part of the population, like the *Literary Digest* election poll mentioned in the video, will suffer from bias due to this **undercoverage**. Misleading results can also be due to **nonresponse** (some subjects can't be contacted or refuse to answer), to badly worded questions, or even to the race, sex, or appearance of the interviewer.

The deliberate use of chance in producing data is intended to eliminate bias. It also makes the outcomes of an experiment or sample survey subject to the laws of probability. The next four units will introduce probability; the final portion of this unit takes a first look at the random behavior of statistical data. First, some basic vocabulary: A number that describes a population is called a **parameter**. A number that can be computed from the data is called a **statistic**. The purpose of sampling or experimentation is usually to use statistics to make statements about unknown parameters.

A statistic from a probability sample or randomized experiment will not take the same value if the sample or experiment is repeated. The **sampling distribution** describes how the statistic varies in repeated data collection. In the video you can watch a sampling distribution build up as repeated SRSs are drawn from a population of beads. Formal statistical inference is based on the sampling distributions of statistics.

**Bias**, which we informally described as "favoritism," can be described more exactly in terms of the sampling distribution. Bias means that the center of the sampling distribution is not equal to the true value of the parameter. We would like to use a statistic that has small bias and also does not vary greatly in repeated sampling or experimenting. The **variability** of the statistic is described by the spread of its sampling distribution. If the sampling distribution is normal, the standard deviation of the distribution describes the variability of the statistic. Properly chosen statistics from randomized data production designs have no bias due to selecting the sample or assigning the experimental units to treatments. The variability of the statistic is determined by the size of the sample or of the experimental groups: larger samples give less variable results. Notice in particular that as long as the population is much larger than the sample, the variability of sample statistics is influenced only by the size of the sample and *not* the by size of the population.

## ASSIGNMENT

1. Read the LEARNING OBJECTIVES to see what specific skills you must acquire from this unit.

2. Read the rest of Section 3.3 and all of Section 3.4 of the text.

3. Do the following problems from the SECTION 3.3 EXERCISES in the text: 3.39, 3.41; and the following problems from the SECTION 3.4 EXERCISES: 3.45, 3.47, 3.49, 3.53, 3.55.

4. Finally, try the SELF-TEST QUESTIONS and compare your answers with those given.

## LEARNING OBJECTIVES

A. Recognize when a stratified sample is appropriate, and use Table B to choose a stratified random sample.

B. Recognize the presence of undercoverage and nonresponse as sources of error in a sample survey, and recognize the effect of the wording of questions on the responses.

C. Identify the parameter and the statistic in a sample or experiment.

D. Describe the bias and variability of a statistic in terms of the mean and spread of its sampling distribution. Understand that the variability of a statistic is controlled by the size of the sample; statistics from larger samples are less variable.

## SELF-TEST QUESTIONS

**14.1** Julie wants to measure student opinion about the state of relations between blacks and whites on her campus. There are 8000 white students and 2000 black students enrolled at the campus. Julie wants to compare black student opinion with white student opinion, so she plans to interview 400 whites and 200 blacks.

Describe the sample design that you would use. Then say how you would label the students in the population. Finally, use Table B to select the first 5 black students and the first 5 white students in your sample.

**14.2** Dr. Pimento wants to know what percent of American college students approve of television advertising. Students who take Psychology 101 at his school are required to serve as research subjects. Dr. Pimento chooses an SRS of 100 from the 900 students taking the course this semester. He asks, "Television as we know it is would not be possible without advertising. Do you agree that having commercials on TV is a fair price to pay for being able to watch it?" Of the 100 students in the sample, 82 answer "Yes."
(a) What is the population in this setting? Describe the parameter and the statistic.
(b) Despite the fact that Dr. Pimento used an SRS, at least two sources of bias are present here. What are they?

**14.3** National opinion polls such as the Gallup Poll usually interview a sample of about 1500 people. Immediately before a presidential election, however, the size of the sample is often increased to about 4000 people. What is the advantage of the larger sample?

**14.4** A news item says, "54% of the people surveyed approved of the president's handling of his office. The margin of error of the poll result is plus or minus three percentage points." The margin of error announced by the polls covers the middle 95% of the sampling distribution of the sample proportion $\hat{p}$. The sampling distribution of $\hat{p}$ is normal. Its mean is equal to the population percent $p$ who approve of the president (no bias). What is the standard deviation of the sampling distribution of $\hat{p}$ in this case?

## SELF-TEST SOLUTIONS

**14.1** This calls for a stratified sample. The two strata are white students and black students. (To keep the problem simple we ignore the other ethnic groups in the student body.) A stratified random sample consists of a separate SRS in each stratum, so we just choose two separate SRSs.

Label the black students 0001–2000 and the white students 0001–8000. To choose the SRS of 200 blacks, enter Table B at line 101 and read four-digit groups. (You can use any line, but be sure to say which line you used.) Only groups between 0001 and 2000 choose students for the sample. The first 5 black students chosen are those labeled

1922, 1927, 0977, 0095, 0056

To choose the SRS of 400 white students, use a different part of the table so that this sample is independent of the sample of blacks. If we enter line 120, the first 5 white students chosen are those with labels

3547, 6559, 7239, 4216, 5850

**14.2** (a) Because Dr. Pimento wants information about "American college students," this is the population. It is better to give a more specific description, such as "undergraduate students enrolled full-time in American degree-granting colleges and universities." The *parameter* is the percent of the *population* who would agree with the statement if asked. The *statistic* is 82%, the percent of the *sample* who agree.
(b) There is serious *undercoverage* because only students in a single course at a single college are sampled. They are not representative of

all American college students. In addition, the *wording of the question* is strongly slanted so as to elicit a "Yes" answer.

**14.3** The results of the larger sample are less variable. The poll can therefore be more confident that the sample statistics (the percents who say they will vote for each candidate) will be close to the truth about the population.

**14.4** By the 68–95–99.7 rule, the middle 95% in any normal distribution lies within $\pm 2$ standard deviations of the mean. Because this margin of error is $\pm 3$ percentage points in this case, the standard deviation is $\sigma = 1.5\% = 0.015$. Notice that $\hat{p} = 0.54 = 54\%$ is simply the result of this specific sample. It is not the mean of the sampling distribution.

# UNIT 15
# WHAT IS PROBABILITY?

## LESSON OVERVIEW

This unit introduces the idea of probability and the basic properties that are shared by all assignments of probability. The next three units look at probability in more depth in preparation for the study of statistical inference.

Some phenomena are **random** in the sense that even though individual outcomes are uncertain, the outcomes of many repetitions follow a regular pattern. So "random" in statistics does not mean simply "haphazard." Probability can be viewed intuitively as relative frequency in many repeated trials of a random phenomenon. Alternatively, a probability can express a personal assessment of chance. Because we are familiar with sampling distributions, we emphasize the interpretation of probability as idealized long-run relative frequency. The video program contrasts personal assessment of chance and long term relative frequency by a story on assessing risks. People's personal assessments of various risks differ greatly from the actual relative frequencies of deaths from these causes. There are clear psychological reasons for this difference. It then explores the meaning of randomness in an interview with Persi Diaconis.

From the idea of probability we turn to the question of how to describe probability with numbers. Although we cannot predict which outcome of a random phenomenon will occur, we can list all of the possible outcomes. This is the **sample space** $S$. Sets of outcomes are called **events.** A **probability model** for a random phenomenon consists of a sample space $S$ and an assignment of probabilities $P$ that assigns a number $P(A)$ to an event $A$ as its probability.

Every assignment of probabilities to events must satisfy several rules that are based on the way relative frequencies behave. The first says that any probability is a number between 0 and 1. The second rule says that the sample space (all possible outcomes) must have probability 1. The third rule says that if two events are **disjoint** (have no outcomes in common), the probability that one or the other occurs is the sum of their individual probabilities. Here are these rules in mathematical form:

(1) $0 \leq P(A) \leq 1$ for any event $A$
(2) $P(S) = 1$
(3) **Addition rule**: If $A$ and $B$ are disjoint events, then

$$P(A \text{ or } B) = P(A) + P(B)$$

The video illustrates these rules with a probability model for the type of driver in cars entering an intersection. This is part of a larger model used by the Federal Highway Administration. This example also illustrates the simplest way to assign probabilities, which can be used when the sample space $S$ has a finite number of individual outcomes: Give every individual outcome a probability and then find the probability of any event by adding the probabilities of the outcomes that make it up.

Remember that the basic rules hold in *all* probability models, not just in very simple models of this kind.

There are rules of probability other than the basic three rules. All of these rules can be derived from the basic three. For example, the probability that an event $A$ does *not* occur is $1 - P(A)$. The event that $A$ does not occur is called the **complement** of $A$, written $A^c$.

(4) **Complement rule:** For any event $A$,

$$P(A^c) = 1 - P(A)$$

## ASSIGNMENT

1. Read the LEARNING OBJECTIVES to see what specific skills you must acquire from this unit.

2. Read the introduction to Chapter 4 of the text and Section 4.1 through Example 4.11.

3. Do the following problems from the SECTION 4.1 EXERCISES in the text: 4.3, 4.7, 4.9, 4.11, 4.14, 4.17.

4. Finally, try the SELF-TEST QUESTIONS and compare your answers with those given.

## LEARNING OBJECTIVES

A. Recognize that some phenomena are random and understand the idea of probability as long term relative frequency.

B. Identify a sample space for simple random phenomena.

C. Decide whether assignments of probabilities to individual outcomes do or do not satisfy the basic laws of probability; assignments that do not satisfy these laws cannot be correct.

D. Calculate the probability of an event from an assignment of probabilities to individual outcomes by adding the probabilities of the outcomes that make up the event.

E. Use the addition rule to find the probability that one or the other of two disjoint events occurs.

F. Use the complements rule to find the probability that an event does not occur.

## SELF-TEST QUESTIONS

**15.1** A medical laboratory tests blood for the presence of antibodies to the AIDS virus. For each blood specimen the outcome is "Yes" or "No." Give a sample space for the results of the next 3 specimens tested.

**15.2** The laboratory tests 800 blood specimens in a week, and counts the number of positive ("Yes") results. This number varies randomly from week to week. Give a sample space for the weekly count of positive AIDS test results.

**15.3** The table below gives two probability models. The left column gives the probabilities that a male worker chosen at random has each of several types of occupation. The right column gives the probability model for the occupation of a female worker chosen at random. Show that one of these is a legitimate probability model and that the other is not.

| Occupation | Male Probability | Female Probability |
|---|---|---|
| Professional | 0.28 | 0.28 |
| Sales, etc. | 0.20 | 0.44 |
| Service | 0.08 | 0.16 |
| Production | 0.21 | 0.03 |
| Operators | 0.19 | 0.09 |

**15.4** Consider the probability model for the occupation of female workers given in Question 15.3.
(a) What is the probability that a randomly selected female worker is a sales worker or a service worker?
(b) What is the probability that she is not a production worker?

**15.5** A difficult probability calculation shows that when a balanced coin is tossed 10 times, the probability that 3 straight heads appear somewhere in the 10 tosses is 0.508. The probability of seeing 3 straight tails is also 0.508.
(a) To find the probability of seeing 3 straight heads *or* 3 straight tails

in 10 tosses, we might add the probabilities of the two events,

$$\begin{aligned} P(A \text{ or } B) &= P(A) + P(B) \\ &= 0.508 + 0.508 = 1.016 \end{aligned}$$

Why do you know that this result is wrong?
(b) Explain why the addition rule for the probability that one or the other of two events occurs does not apply in this case.

## SELF-TEST SOLUTIONS

**15.1** The sample space is just the collection of all possible outcomes. Let Y stand for "Yes" and N stand for "No." The sample space is

$S$={YYY, YYN, YNY, YNN, NYY, NYN, NNY, NNN}

(If you just *count* the number of "Yes" results, you get a simpler $S$, as in the next question, but this question does not ask you to simply count results.)

**15.2** The number of positive test results can be any whole number between 0 (no positives) and 800 (all positives). In mathematical notation, this is written

$S=\{0, 1, 2, \ldots, 799, 800\}$

**15.3** An assignment of probabilities to the individual outcomes in a finite sample space must assign a probability between 0 and 1 to each outcome, and the probabilities assigned must add to 1.

The male probabilities are all between 0 and 1, but their sum is 0.96. This is not a legitimate probability model. The female probabilities are all between 0 and 1 and their sum is 1. This is a legitimate probability model.

**15.4** To find the probability of any event, add the probabilities of the outcomes that make up the event.
(a) The probability that she is a sales or service worker is

$$0.44 + 0.16 = 0.60$$

(b) If $A$ is the event that she is a production worker, the question asks for $P(A^c)$. By the complement rule, this is

$$1 - P(A) = 1 - 0.03 = 0.97$$

You can also find this probability by adding the probabilities of all occupations other than production: 0.28+0.44+0.16+0.09=0.97.

**15.5** (a) The answer is greater than 1. This must be wrong, because no probability can be greater than 1.
(b) The addition rule applies only to *disjoint* events. The events "3 straight heads in 10 tosses" and "3 straight tails in 10 tosses" are not disjoint, because it is possible for both of these events to occur in 10 tosses of a coin. For example, both occur if the outcome of the 10 tosses is

H, T, T, T, T, H, H, H, T, H

# UNIT 16
# RANDOM VARIABLES

## LESSON OVERVIEW

This unit opens with an additional important general rule of probability, which gives the probability that *both* of two events occur. Like the addition rule, this rule holds for only special circumstances. Events $A$ and $B$ are called **independent** if knowing whether one event occurs does not change the probability we would assign to the other event.

> **Multiplication rule**: If events $A$ and $B$ are independent, then $P(A \text{ and } B) = P(A)P(B)$

The video program first illustrates *lack* of independence by a look at an incident in which several students made the same errors on a national examination and were therefore accused of cheating. The students had the same teacher, so the common errors were not highly improbable. Independence and the multiplication rule are then applied to studying the reliability of systems with many parts: the multiplication rule shows that the probability of all parts performing well is very small. The video looks at the *Challenger* space shuttle disaster from this point of view. In watching the video program, pay particular attention to the distinction between disjoint events (the addition rule holds) and independent events (the multiplication rule applies).

We then turn to the kinds of probability models that are most useful in statistics. A **random variable** is a numerical outcome of a random phenomenon. Many probability models take $S$ to be all possible values of a random variable $X$ and define $P$ from the **probability distribution** of $X$. Statistics from a sample or experiment are examples of random variables.

A random variable $X$ and its distribution can be discrete or continuous. A **discrete random variable** takes a finite collection of values. The probability distribution assigns each of these values a probability between 0 and 1 such that the sum of all the probabilities assigned is 1. The probability of an event $A$ is then the sum of the probabilities of all the values that make up $A$. This kind of probability model is similar to those we met in the previous unit. The second type of random variable uses a new way of assigning probability: as areas under a curve. A **continuous random variable** takes all values in some interval of real numbers. The probability distribution assigns to an event $A$ the area above $A$ and under a **density curve**. The height of a density curve must be 0 or positive everywhere, and the curve must have total area 1 beneath it.

The video shows how discrete distributions can be pictured by histograms and continuous distributions by smooth density curves. **Normal distributions** are one type of continuous probability distribution. Predictions of the time $X$ at which the next major earthquake will occur are expressed by giving the density curve for the random variable $X$. The distribution of a random variable has a mean $\mu$ and a standard deviation $\sigma$, just as distributions of data have a mean $\overline{x}$ and a standard deviation $s$. In the case of discrete random variables, it is easy to calculate $\mu$ and $\sigma$ from the assignment of probabilities to outcomes.

## ASSIGNMENT

1. Read the LEARNING OBJECTIVES to see what specific skills you must acquire from this unit.

2. Read the remaining part of Section 4.1, all of Section 4.2, and Section 4.3 omitting the subsections on "Rules for Means" and "Rules for variances." The remaining topics in Section 4.3 will be covered in the next unit.

3. Do the following problems from the SECTION 4.1 EXERCISES in the text: 4.22, 4.25, 4.29; the following problems from the SECTION 4.2 EXERCISES: 4.31, 4.37, 4.43; and the following problem from the SECTION 4.3 EXERCISES: 4.57.

4. Finally, try the SELF-TEST QUESTIONS and compare your answers with those given.

## LEARNING OBJECTIVES

A. Recognize when it is reasonable to assume that events are independent.

B. Use the multiplication rule to find the probability that all of several independent events occur.

C. Express a random numerical outcome as the value of a random variable and recognize whether the random variable is discrete or continuous.

D. Recognize when the distribution of a discrete random variable is legitimate and calculate probabilities of events from such a distribution.

E. Calculate the mean and standard deviation of a discrete random variable from its probability distribution.

F. Understand how the distribution of a continuous random variable assigns probabilities as areas under a density curve.

## SELF-TEST QUESTIONS

**16.1** A plant breeder is producing hybrid tomato plants. Each offspring from a particular cross has probability 3/4 of being fusarium-resistant and probability 1/2 of being tender-fruited. Inheritance of these two characteristics is independent.
(a) What is the probability that a plant is both fusarium-resistant and tender-fruited?
(b) What is the probability that a plant is neither fusarium-resistant nor tender-fruited?

**16.2** Sarah and Erin are among eight young executives competing for promotion to two managerial positions in their firm. Both Sarah and Erin have worked in marketing, while the other candidates have backgrounds in finance or sales. Let $A$ be the event that Sarah wins one of the positions and $B$ the event that Erin is one of those chosen. Are the events $A$ and $B$ disjoint? Is it reasonable to assume that they are independent?

**16.3** Is each of the following random variable best described as discrete or continuous?
(a) A technician examines a drop of blood under a microscope and counts the number $X$ of red blood cells in a fixed area marked on the slide.
(b) Another specimen of blood is analyzed chemically to report the level $Y$ of triglycerides in milligrams per deciliter of blood.

**16.4** A health maintenance organization (HMO) offers an unlimited number of visits to its member physicians for a fixed annual medical insurance payment. As part of its planning, the HMO records the number of office visits made in January to its physicians by each of the 120,000 people it covers. The distribution of the count $X$ of visits is as follows.

| Count | 0 | 1 | 2 | 3 | 4 | 5 | 6 | 7 |
|---|---|---|---|---|---|---|---|---|
| Probability | .25 | .23 | .18 | .16 | .08 | .04 | .03 | .03 |

Display the distribution of $X$ in a probability histogram. Then find the mean and the standard deviation of $X$.

# SELF-TEST SOLUTIONS

**16.1** The multiplication rule for independent events applies in both parts of the problem. Call $A$ the event that the offspring plant is fusarium-resistant and $B$ the event that it is tender-fruited. Because $A$ and $B$ are independent, so are their complements $A^c$ and $B^c$.
(a) $P(A \text{ and } B) = P(A)P(B) = (3/4)(1/2) = 3/8 = 0.375$.
(b) $P(A^c \text{ and } B^c) = P(A^c)P(B^c) = (1/4)(1/2) = 1/8 = 0.125$.

**16.2** Because two positions are available, it is possible for *both* Sarah and Erin to be promoted. The events $A$ and $B$ are therefore not disjoint. Sarah and Erin have similar backgrounds, so that if the two positions require different skills it is likely that only one of them will be chosen. So it is reasonable to assume that knowing that Sarah has been chosen (event $A$ occurs) lowers the probability that Erin is promoted (event $B$). This means that $A$ and $B$ are not independent.

Notice that we can be sure that the events are not disjoint. But independence is usually assumed as part of a probability model, so the question is whether it is a reasonable assumption in this case. It is possible to assign probabilities so that $A$ and $B$ are independent, but this is not a reasonable assumption based on the information that is given.

**16.3** (a) $X$ is a count, so it can take only whole number values 0, 1, 2, ... So $X$ is certainly discrete.
(b) The level of a substance in the blood is not restricted to a discrete set of values, but can have any value in an entire interval. So $Y$ is continuous. (The actual analysis probably reports $Y$ only to limited accuracy, with values like 20.011, 20.012, ..., so that $Y$ as reported could be taken to be discrete. It is simpler to think of $Y$ as continuous.)

**16.4** The probability histogram appears in Figure 16.1. There is a bar for each possible outcome, and the height of each bar is the probability of that outcome.

The mean of the discrete random variable $X$ is

$$\begin{aligned}\mu_X &= x_1p_1 + x_2p_2 + \cdots + x_kp_k \\ &= (0)(.25) + (1)(.23) + \cdots + (7)(.03) \\ &= 1.98\end{aligned}$$

The variance of $X$ is the mean of the squared deviations $(x_i - \mu_X)^2$ of the values of $X$ from the mean, which is

$$\begin{aligned}\sigma_X^2 &= (x_1-\mu)^2p_1 + (x_2-\mu)^2p_2 + \cdots + (x_k-\mu)^2p_k \\ &= (0-1.98)^2(.25) + (1-1.98)^2(.23) + \cdots + (7-1.98)^2(.03) \\ &= .9801 + .2209 + \cdots + .7560 = 3.2996\end{aligned}$$

The standard deviation is the square root of the variance,

$$\sigma_X = \sqrt{3.2996} = 1.8165$$

Figure 16.1

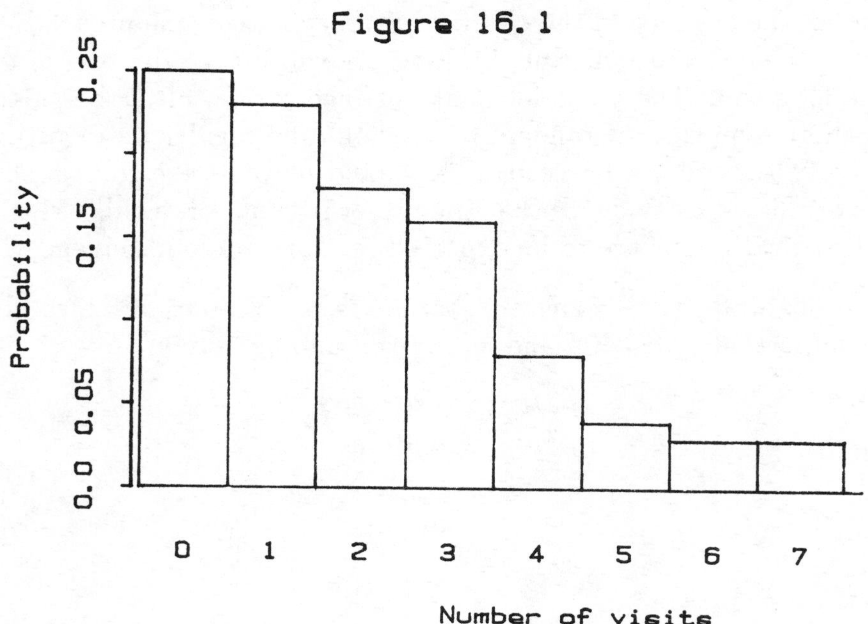

# UNIT 17
# BINOMIAL DISTRIBUTIONS

## LESSON OVERVIEW

The mean $\mu_X$ of a random variable $X$ was introduced in the previous unit as the average of the possible outcomes of $X$ weighted by their probability of occurrence. The **law of large numbers** says that $\mu_X$ is the average outcome in another sense as well: the actually observed mean outcome in many independent trials must approach $\mu_X$. In the long run, observed relative frequencies of events approach the probabilities of the events and the observed average outcome approaches the mean of the distribution. But this kind of regular behavior occurs *only* in the long run. The video looks at our incorrect intuitive belief that even short sequences of random trials should be regular by investigating the "hot hand" in basketball. Fans and players take runs of shots made or missed as evidence that the player is "hot" or "cold," when in fact these variations are to be expected in short random sequences.

Like probability, the means and variances of random variables obey some important rules. If $a$ and $b$ are fixed numbers, then

$$\begin{aligned} \mu_{a+bX} &= a + b\mu_X \\ \sigma^2_{a+bX} &= b^2\sigma^2_X \end{aligned}$$

If $X$ and $Y$ are any two random variables, then

$$\mu_{X+Y} = \mu_X + \mu_Y$$

If $X$ and $Y$ are *independent*, then

$$\sigma^2_{X+Y} = \sigma^2_X + \sigma^2_Y$$

$$\sigma^2_{X-Y} = \sigma^2_X + \sigma^2_Y$$

Note that the addition rule for means always holds, but the addition rule for variances need not be true if $X$ and $Y$ are not independent. The video applies these rules when $X$ and $Y$ are the rates of return on two different investments.

We now know enough general probability to turn to some specific distributions that are important in statistics. The **binomial distribution** $B(n, p)$ is the distribution of the count $X$ of successes in $n$ independent trials each having probability $p$ of success. "Success" is shorthand for any outcome we are interested in, such as heads in tossing a coin or "yes" answers to an opinion poll question. The video shows how a binomial distribution is produced by a quincunx, in which balls strike pegs as they fall and are deflected either to the left or to the right. A "success" here means falling to the right, so the bin in which the ball lands at the bottom of the quincunx counts the number of successes.

The binomial distributions are discrete; the possible values of $X$ are the whole numbers from 0 to $n$. There is a different binomial distribution for each value of $n$ and $p$. You can find binomial probabilities in Table C at the back of the text. The text also gives a formula for binomial probabilities, but you need not learn this formula. When the number of trials $n$ is large, a binomial distribution is closely approximated by a normal distribution. This is a convenient way to calculate binomial probabilities in many cases. In the video program, binomial distributions describe the number of children with sickle cell anemia in families whose parents are carriers of this genetic defect. Each child of such parents has probability $p = 0.25$ of inheriting the disease.

The mean and standard deviation of a binomial count $X$ and a sample proportion of successes $\hat{p} = X/n$ are

$$\begin{aligned} \mu_X &= np \\ \sigma_X &= \sqrt{np(1-p)} \\ \mu_{\hat{p}} &= p \\ \sigma_{\hat{p}} &= \sqrt{\frac{p(1-p)}{n}} \end{aligned}$$

Remember that these convenient formulas are only good for binomial distributions, not for discrete distributions in general.

## ASSIGNMENT

1. Read the LEARNING OBJECTIVES to see what specific skills you must acquire from this unit.

2. Read Section 4.3 again, concentrating on the subsections "Rules for Means" and "Rules for Variances" and read Section 5.1 of the text, omitting the starred optional material on "Binomial Probabilities" and "The Continuity correction."

3. Do the following problems from the SECTION 4.3 EXERCISES in the text: 4.55, 4.59; and the following problems from the SECTION 5.1 EXERCISES: 5.1, 5.5, 5.13, 5.15.

4. Finally, try the SELF-TEST QUESTIONS and compare your answers with those given.

## LEARNING OBJECTIVES

A. Know the law of large numbers and recognize when it does and does not apply.

B. Use the rules for means to obtain the mean of a sum of random variables.

C. Use the rules for variances to obtain the variance of a sum of independent random variables.

D. Recognize when a binomial distribution is appropriate and identify $n$ and $p$.

E. Find binomial probabilities from a table.

F. Calculate the mean and standard deviation of a binomial distribution.

G. Recognize when the normal approximation to a binomial distribution can be applied, and use it to calculate binomial probabilities.

# SELF-TEST QUESTIONS

**17.1** A garden center advertises that 90% of its dogwood seedlings will survive when given normal care. The survival of a seedling given normal care is independent of the survival of other seedlings.
(a) If a homeowner plants 10 such seedlings, what is the probability that at least 9 will survive?
(b) An apartment complex plants 100 of these seedlings. What is the probability that at least 92 will survive?

**17.2** A bet of \$1 on "red" in roulette has mean outcome −\$0.053, that is, a mean loss of 5.3 cents.
(a) Explain to a friend who knows no statistics what the law of large numbers says about the result of making a large number of \$1 bets.
(b) After listening to your explanation, your friend says, "I see. The mean is pretty small, so if I make a lot of bets I'm nearly certain not to lose very much." Is your friend correct? Why or why not?

**17.3** Some of the earliest studies of probability were done by the eccentric Italian mathematician Girolamo Cardano (1501–1576). One of the many dice games that Cardano studied was played with 6 six-sided dice. Each of these dice had 5 blank faces and one face with a number; the numbers 1 to 6 each appeared on one of the dice. All 6 dice were rolled at once, and the payoff to the gambler was based on the total of the numbers showing on the up faces.
(a) Consider the die with 5 blank faces and the number 3 on the sixth face. If $X_3$ is the outcome of rolling this die once (blank faces count 0), give the probability distribution of $X_3$ and find its mean and variance.
(b) Starting from your work in (a), find the mean of the total obtained by rolling all 6 dice *without* finding the probability distribution of this total.

(c) Is it reasonable to assume that the outcomes of the 6 dice are independent? Did your work in (b) use the fact of independence?
(d) The variances of the outcomes for the other five dice are:

| Number on die | Variance |
|---|---|
| 1 | 0.139 |
| 2 | 0.556 |
| 4 | 2.222 |
| 5 | 3.472 |
| 6 | 5.000 |

Use this information to find the standard deviation of the total that appears when all 6 dice are rolled.

## SELF-TEST SOLUTIONS

**17.1** (a) The count of surviving seedlings is the count of successes in $n$ independent trials each having probability 0.9 of a success. Because $p =$ .09 is not in Table C, count seedlings that die instead. Call the count of dead seedlings $Y$; $Y$ has the binomial distribution with parameters $n$ and $p = 0.1$. From Table C,

$$\begin{aligned} P(Y \leq 1) &= P(Y = 0) + P(Y = 1) \\ &= .3487 + .3874 = 0.7361 \end{aligned}$$

(b) Now $n = 100$ so that use of the table is not possible. We can count seedlings that live. Call the count of live seedlings $X$; $X$ has the binomial distribution with $n = 100$ and $p = 0.9$. Because $np = 90$ and $n(1 - p) = 10$ are both at least 10, the normal approximation to the binomial distribution is quite accurate. The mean and standard deviation of $X$ are

$$\begin{aligned}\mu &= np = (100)(.9) = 90 \\ \sigma &= \sqrt{np(1-p)} = \sqrt{(100)(.9)(.1)} = 3\end{aligned}$$

The normal approximation takes $X$ to have the $N(90, 3)$ distribution. Here is the probability (without the continuity correction).

$$\begin{aligned}P(X \geq 92) &= P(\frac{X-90}{3} \geq \frac{92-90}{3}) \\ &= P(Z \geq .67) \\ &= 1 - .7486 = 0.2514\end{aligned}$$

**17.2** (a) In a large number of bets, your average outcome is sure to be very close to a loss of 5.3 cents on each bet.
(b) No—if the *average* is close to a loss of 5.3 cents per bet, you can expect your losses to keep on growing as you make more bets. In 1000 bets you expect a loss of about \$53, and in 10,000 bets a loss of about \$530.

Here's a fine point: Notice, for example, that when the average is between 5.2 and 5.4 cents per bet, the amount lost in \$1000 bets is between \$52 and \$54 and the amount lost in 10,000 bets is between \$520 and \$540. Saying that the *average* is close to 5.3 cents still allows the *total* loss in dollars to vary by a larger amount when you make more bets. It's important to talk in terms of the average of many outcomes when applying the law of large numbers.

**17.3** (a) The discrete probability distribution of $X_3$ is

| Outcome | 0 | 1 |
|---|---|---|
| Probability | 5/6 | 1/6 |

The mean is therefore

$$\mu_3 = (0)(\frac{5}{6}) + (3)(\frac{1}{6}) = \frac{3}{6} = .5$$

The variance is

$$\begin{aligned}\sigma_3^2 &= (0 - .5)^2(\frac{5}{6}) + (3 - .5)^2(\frac{1}{6}) \\ &= .2083 + 1.0417 = 1.25\end{aligned}$$

(b) The total is the sum of the numbers appearing on the up faces of the 6 dice. As in (a), let these numbers for the separate dice be $X_1$ for the die with 5 blank faces and a 1, $X_2$ for the die with 5 blank faces and a 2, and so on. Then the total is

$$X = X_1 + X_2 + X_3 + X_4 + X_5 + X_6$$

and the addition rule for means says that the mean outcome is the sum of the means for the individual dice. These individual means are found just as in (a). They are:

$$\begin{aligned}\mu_1 &= (1)(\frac{1}{6}) = \frac{1}{6} \\ \mu_2 &= (2)(\frac{1}{6}) = \frac{2}{6} \\ \mu_3 &= (3)(\frac{1}{6}) = \frac{3}{6} \\ \mu_4 &= (4)(\frac{1}{6}) = \frac{4}{6} \\ \mu_5 &= (5)(\frac{1}{6}) = \frac{5}{6} \\ \mu_6 &= (6)(\frac{1}{6}) = \frac{6}{6}\end{aligned}$$

The mean outcome is therefore

$$\begin{aligned}\mu_X &= \frac{1}{6} + \frac{2}{6} + \cdots + \frac{6}{6} \\ &= \frac{21}{6} = 3\frac{1}{2}\end{aligned}$$

(c) Because the dice do not influence each other, their outcomes are independent. The addition rule for means that was used in (b) does *not* require independence. It is true even if the random variables are dependent.
(d) The addition rule for variances *does* require independence. In this case, the variance of the sum can be found as the sum of the variances for the individual dice because the dice are independent. This variance is

$$\sigma_X^2 = .139 + .556 + 1.25 + 2.22 + 3.472 + 5 = 12.639$$

Don't forget to include your result for $X_3$ from (a). The standard deviation is

$$\sigma = \sqrt{12.639} = 3.555$$

Remember that standard deviations do *not* add—you must add the variances and take the square root.

# UNIT 18
# THE SAMPLE MEAN AND CONTROL CHARTS

## LESSON OVERVIEW

Sample counts and proportions, which were discussed in Unit 17, are important sample statistics. This unit presents the facts about another very important statistic, the sample mean $\overline{x}$. Suppose we have an SRS of size $n$ drawn from a large population with mean $\mu$ and standard deviation $\sigma$. Here are the big facts about the sampling distribution of the mean $\overline{x}$ of the sample:

- $\overline{x}$ has mean and standard deviation given by

$$\mu_{\overline{x}} = \mu$$
$$\sigma_{\overline{x}} = \frac{\sigma}{\sqrt{n}}$$

- If the population distribution is normal, so is the sampling distribution of $\overline{x}$.

- In any case, the distribution of $\overline{x}$ is approximately normal when the sample size $n$ is large. This is the **central limit theorem.**

The first fact says that the sample mean $\overline{x}$ is an unbiased estimator of the population mean $\mu$ and that the variability of a sample mean decreases as the sample size increases. The second and third facts both concern the form of the distribution of $\overline{x}$. It turns out that any sum, difference, or average of *independent* normal random variables also has a normal distribution. This leads to the second fact: If the population has a normal distribution $N(\mu, \sigma)$, then $\overline{x}$ has the $N(\mu, \sigma/\sqrt{n})$ distribution. What if the population does not have a normal distribution? The central limit theorem states that for large $n$ the sampling distribution of $\overline{x}$ is approximately $N(\mu, \sigma/\sqrt{n})$ for any population with finite standard deviation $\sigma$. This is true even if the population distribution is discrete.

In the video program, the central limit theorem is applied to playing roulette in a casino. Because the standard deviation $\sigma$ of the payoff on a single play is large, the standard deviation $\sigma/\sqrt{n}$ remains large for $n = 50$ or so bets. Gambling is exciting for the gambler because the outcome of an evening's betting is uncertain. But the casino bets a very large number of times. So $\sigma/\sqrt{n}$ for the casino is very small and the average payoff $\overline{x}$ will be very close to the mean $\mu$. The mean favors the casino a bit, so in the long run it makes money at a predictable rate.

These facts about the distribution of $\overline{x}$ are applied in **statistical process control** to help monitor and improve the quality of manufactured goods. The idea is to watch the manufacturing process to catch changes early rather than waiting to inspect the product at the end. A process that can be measured over time is **in control** if its pattern of variation (its probability distribution) is the same at all times. A process that is in control is operating under stable conditions.

An $\overline{x}$ **control chart** is a graph of sample means plotted against the time order of the samples to show whether the level of the process is changing over time. The chart has a solid center line at the target value $\mu$ of the process mean and dashed **control limits** at $\mu \pm 3\sigma/\sqrt{n}$. The control limits include the range of variation in $\overline{x}$ that we expect to see in a normally operating process. A value outside these limits suggests that the process has been disturbed by some additional source of variation that should be located and fixed. So an $\overline{x}$ chart helps us decide if a process is in control with mean $\mu$ and standard deviation $\sigma$. In practice, an out of control signal results either when any point falls outside the control limits or when a **run** of 9 consecutive points on the same side of the center line occurs. In the video program, you will see control charts in use to monitor the salt content of potato chips.

## ASSIGNMENT

1. Read the LEARNING OBJECTIVES to see what specific skills you must acquire from this unit.

2. Read Sections 5.2 and 5.3 of the text.

3. Do the following problems from the SECTION 5.2 EXERCISES in the text: 5.25, 5.27, 5.33, 5.41, 5.43; and the following problem from the SECTION 5.3 EXERCISES: 5.51.

4. Finally, try the SELF-TEST QUESTIONS and compare your answers with those given.

## LEARNING OBJECTIVES

A. Find the mean and standard deviation of a sample mean $\overline{x}$ when the mean $\mu$ and standard deviation $\sigma$ of the population are known.

B. Understand that $\overline{x}$ has a normal distribution when the population distribution is normal or when the sample is large (central limit theorem); use this normal distribution to calculate probabilities that concern $\overline{x}$.

C. Use the fact that any sum or difference of independent normal variables has a normal distribution to calculate probabilities that concern such sums or differences.

D. Construct an $\overline{x}$ control chart when target values $\mu$ and $\sigma$ are given and identify lack of control on such a chart.

## SELF-TEST QUESTIONS

**18.1** Errors in careful measurements often have a distribution that is close to normal. Experience shows that the error in a certain surveying method varies when a measurement is repeated according to a normal distribution with mean 0 (that is, the procedure does not systematically overestimate or underestimate the true length) and standard deviation 0.03 meter. A measurement is repeated 3 times and the average of the three measurements is used as the final value.
(a) What is the mean error in the final value? What is the standard

deviation of this value?
(b) What is the probability that this procedure gives a result that is accurate to within ±0.01 meter?

**18.2** A sample survey asks a sample of urban residents and a sample of rural residents if they are afraid to go outside at night near their home because of crime. Suppose that in fact 23% of all rural residents and 64% of all urban residents would say "Yes" to this question. The sampling design allows the survey's statisticians to calculate the following information in this case: The proportion $\hat{p}_1$ of the rural sample who say "Yes" varies normally with mean 0.23 and standard deviation 0.018 and the proportion $\hat{p}_2$ of "Yes" responses in the urban sample has a normal distribution with mean 0.64 and standard deviation 0.013. What is the probability that the urban-rural difference $D = \hat{p}_2 - \hat{p}_1$ in the samples is at least 40 percentage points?

**18.3** When a certain process is in control, it produces measurements that are normally distributed with mean $\mu = 1.50$ centimeter (cm) and standard deviation $\sigma = 0.20$ cm. A sample of 4 measurements is made each hour in order to keep an $\overline{x}$ control chart.
(a) Give the center line and control limits for the $\overline{x}$ chart.
(b) The next 20 hours give the following values of $\overline{x}$. Draw the control chart with these points plotted on it. Is there any indication that the process is out of control? At what point does the control chart signal lack of control?

| Hour | 1 | 2 | 3 | 4 | 5 | 6 | 7 | 8 | 9 | 10 |
|---|---|---|---|---|---|---|---|---|---|---|
| $\overline{x}$ | 1.60 | 1.54 | 1.31 | 1.45 | 1.40 | 1.61 | 1.47 | 1.45 | 1.45 | 1.52 |
| **Hour** | **11** | **12** | **13** | **14** | **15** | **16** | **17** | **18** | **19** | **20** |
| $\overline{x}$ | 1.66 | 1.72 | 1.63 | 1.60 | 1.76 | 1.71 | 1.61 | 1.63 | 1.60 | 1.76 |

# SELF-TEST SOLUTIONS

**18.1** It is reasonable to assume that the three measurements are independent of each other. The final value is their sample mean. The error in this final value is just the sample mean $\overline{x}$ of the errors in the three individual measurements. Each of the individual errors has the $N(0, .03)$ distribution.

(a) The mean and standard deviation of a sample mean are

$$\begin{aligned} \mu_{\overline{x}} &= \mu = 0 \\ \sigma_{\overline{x}} &= \frac{\sigma}{\sqrt{n}} = \frac{0.03}{\sqrt{3}} = 0.0173 \end{aligned}$$

(b) The average $\overline{x}$ of the three measurements has the $N(0, .0173)$ distribution. This is true because the individual measurements are normal and so their average is also normal. Therefore

$$\begin{aligned} P(-.01 \leq \overline{x} \leq .01) &= P\left(\frac{-.01 - 0}{.0173} \leq Z \leq \frac{.01 - 0}{.0173}\right) \\ &= P(-.58 \leq Z \leq .58) \\ &= .7190 - .2810 = 0.4380 \end{aligned}$$

**18.2** The rural and urban results are independent of each other. The difference $D$ is the difference between two independent normal variables and therefore has a normal distribution. The mean is the difference in means,

$$\mu_D = .64 - .23 = .41$$

The variance is the *sum* of the variances

$$\sigma_D^2 = .018^2 + .013^2 = 0.000493$$

The standard deviation of the difference $D$ is $\sigma_D = \sqrt{.000493} = 0.0222$. We now know that $D$ has the $N(.41, .0222)$ distribution. The probability we want is then found from Table A after standardizing $D$.

$$\begin{aligned} P(D \geq .40) &= P\left(\frac{D - .41}{.0222} \geq \frac{.40 - .41}{.0222}\right) \\ &= P(Z \geq -.45) \\ &= 1 - .3264 = 0.6736 \end{aligned}$$

This problem is a good test of your knowledge of probability because it requires you to combine several facts in one problem. You must recognize independence, find the mean and standard deviation using the addition rules, and then formulate the probability needed and find it using the normal tables.

**18.3** (a) The center line is at $\mu = 1.50$. The control limits are

$$\begin{aligned} \mu \pm 3\frac{\sigma}{\sqrt{n}} &= 1.50 \pm 3\frac{0.20}{\sqrt{4}} \\ &= 1.50 \pm 0.30 \\ &= 1.2 \text{ and } 1.8 \end{aligned}$$

(b) The $\overline{x}$ chart appears in Figure 18.1. There are no points outside the control limits. But the last 11 points all lie above the center line. This is very unlikely to occur if the mean remains at 1.5, so it is evidence of lack of control. The *runs* criterion signals loss of control when 9 consecutive points above the center line are observed; this happens at Hour 18 in this case.

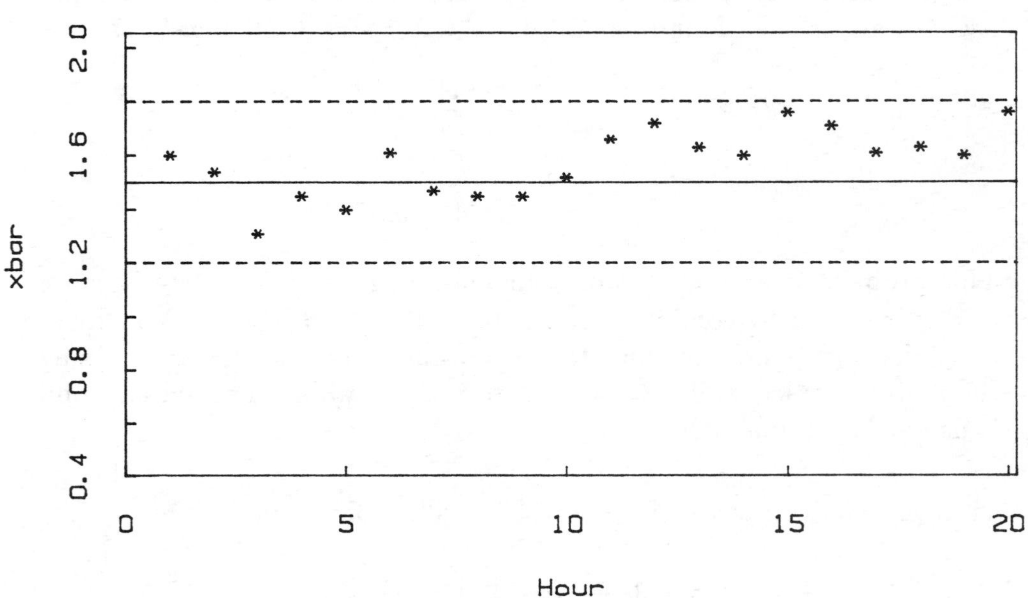
Figure 18.1
xbar
2.0
1.6
1.2
0.8
0.4
0
5
10
15
20
Hour

# SAMPLE EXAMINATION 2

The second sample examination covers the material of Units 11 to 18. You should review the text sections from Chapters 2 to 5 that were assigned in those units. The following problems from the CHAPTER EXERCISES in these chapters will help you review: 2.98, 3.61, 3.65, 4.89, 4.93, 5.61, 5.63, 5.70, 5.71. Then work SAMPLE EXAMINATION 2 under examination conditions, that is, without referring to the text unless your course gives open book examinations. Compare your answers with the solutions given, and review again any material that proved difficult.

## PART I–MULTIPLE CHOICE–2 POINTS EACH

An advertising agency conducts a sample survey to see how adult women react to various adjectives that might be used to describe an automobile. The firm chooses 300 women from across the country. Each woman is read a list of adjectives, such as "elegant" and "prestigious." For each adjective she must indicate how desirable a car described this way seems to her. The possible answers she can give are (1) Highly desirable, (2) Somewhat desirable, (3) Neutral, and (4) Not desirable.

**1** The population in this sample survey is
(a) the adjectives that are tested
(b) the 300 women interviewed
(c) the various makes of automobiles
(d) all adult women

**2** The response variable in this sample survey is
(a) how desirable the car seems
(b) the 300 women

(c) the adjectives that are tested
(d) all adult women

**3** Of the 300 women interviewed in this survey, 76% said that a car described as "elegant" was highly desirable. The number 76% is a
(a) margin of error
(b) parameter
(c) statistic
(d) bias

**4** The random variable $X$ records which answer a woman gives for the adjective "elegant." $X$ is
(a) a continuous random variable
(b) a discrete random variable
(c) a binomial random variable
(d) a normal random variable
(e) both (b) and (c)

**5** A medical researcher thinks that adding calcium to the diet will help reduce blood pressure. She believes that the effect may be different for blacks and whites. Twenty black men and 20 white men are willing to participate in the study. The researcher chooses 10 of the blacks and 10 of the whites at random. These men take a calcium pill every day. The other 20 men take a placebo. This is a
(a) completely randomized experimental design
(b) randomized block experimental design
(c) stratified random sample design
(d) simple random sample design

**6** Near election time, the Gallup Poll increases the size of its samples from about 1500 people to about 4000 people. The purpose of this is

(a) to reduce the bias of the result
(b) to increase the bias of the result
(c) to reduce the variability of the result
(d) to increase the variability of the result

**7** A table of random digits has the following property
(a) 9999 will never occur anywhere in the table
(b) the probability that 9999 are the first four digits in a line is 0.0001
(c) each 100 entries in the table have exactly ten 9's
(d) none of these is true

**8** An important advantage of experiments over observational studies is
(a) experiments are usually less expensive
(b) experiments are more realistic
(c) experiments are easier to design and carry out
(d) experiments can give good evidence for causation

**9** You roll a single fair die (six faces, all equally probable) 6000 times. Which of the following statements is correct?
(a) The number of rolls on which a 3 comes up will be very close to 1000
(b) About 1/6 of the rolls will give a 3
(c) After five consecutive 3's, the probability that the next roll gives a 3 is very small
(d) All of the above

**10** A machine that caps bottles has probability 0.002 of not sealing the cap properly. Each bottle is sealed independently of all other bottles. Which of the following variables have binomial distributions?
(a) The number of unsealed caps in the next 1000 bottles
(b) The number of bottles processed before the first unsealed cap

(c) The number of properly sealed caps in a case of 24 bottles
(d) Both (a) and (c)
(e) All of (a), (b), and (c)

**11** The weight of two year-old children has mean 26 pounds and standard deviation 2 pounds, but is not normally distributed. The standard deviation of the average weight of 5 randomly chosen two year-olds is
(a) 0.4 pounds
(b) 0.89 pounds
(c) 2 pounds
(d) can't calculate the result because the population is not normal
(e) none of the above

**12** An estate is protected by two alarm systems which function independently of each other. System A has probability 0.9 of sounding an alarm when an intruder enters the grounds. System B has probability 0.8 of sounding an alarm in the same circumstances. What is the probability that *neither* system sounds an alarm when an intruder enters?
(a) 0.02
(b) 0.72
(c) 0.30
(d) 0.28
(e) none of the above

**13** A grocery store lottery game gives you probability 0.05 of winning a prize each time you visit the store. If you visit the store 5 times, what is the probability that you win at least once?
(a) 0.05
(b) 0.2036
(c) 0.2262
(d) 0.25

(e) none of the above

**14** The most important advantage of a census of all U.S. households over a large sample of households is that
(a) a census gives more accurate information about the average characteristics of all households
(b) a census gives information about every small area within the country
(c) a census is cheaper and faster
(d) none—a census has no important advantages over a large sample

**15** You have data on the faculty of a university classified by their sex and the department in which they teach. You can report the association between sex and department by
(a) comparing the percent of female faculty in each department
(b) giving the correlation $r$ between sex and department
(c) giving the marginal distribution of faculty by department
(d) giving the marginal distribution of faculty by sex

**16** A telephone survey uses random digit dialing equipment that dials residential telephones in Los Angeles at random. In Los Angeles 1/3 of all residential telephones have unlisted numbers. What does the law of large numbers say about the next 12 numbers dialed by the survey?
(a) exactly 1/3 of the 12 will be unlisted
(b) close to 1/3 will be unlisted
(c) if all of the first 4 are unlisted, few if any of the next 8 will be unlisted
(d) nothing—the law of large numbers says nothing about only 12 trials

**17** A sample survey chooses a sample of households and measures their annual income and their savings. Some events of interest are:

$A$ = the household chosen has income at least \$50,000
$C$ = the household chosen has at least \$10,000 in savings

The event $A^c$ is the event that a household
(a) has income at least \$50,000
(b) has income less than \$50,000
(c) has income at least \$50,000 and savings at least \$10,000
(d) is not selected by the sample survey

**18** We say that a manufacturing process is *in control* when
(a) there is no variation at all in the items being produced
(b) there is some variation, but all of the items are of good quality
(c) there is some variation, but the distribution remains the same over time
(d) there is some variation, but the variation is as small as the process is capable of

**19** The distribution of weight for two year-old children has mean 26 pounds and standard deviation 2 pounds, but is not normal. In writing a report, you must give this information in kilograms rather than pounds. One kilogram is 2.2 pounds, and one pound is 0.45 kilograms. The mean weight in kilograms is
(a) about 57.2 kg
(b) about 11.8 kg
(c) about 125.8 kg
(d) can't do the calculation because the distribution is not normal
(e) none of the above

**20** The standard deviation of the distribution of weights in kilograms in Problem 19 is

(a) about 0.91 kg
(b) about 4.4 kg
(c) about 19.4 kg
(d) can't do the calculation because the distribution is not normal
(d) none of the above

# PART II

**1** (18 points) Turkeys raised commercially for food are often fed the antibiotic salinomycin to prevent infections from spreading among the birds. Salinomycin can damage the birds' internal organs, especially the pancreas. A researcher believes that a combination of selenium and vitamin E in the diet may prevent injury. He wants to explore the effects of two levels (call them $S_1$ and $S_2$) of selenium in combination with any of three levels (call them $E_1$, $E_2$, and $E_3$) of vitamin E added to the diet of turkeys. There are 30 turkeys available for the study. At the end of the study, the birds will be killed and their pancreas examined under a microscope.
(a) (5) How many factors does this experiment have? How many treatments? Give a table that identifies each of the treatments.
(b) (7) Outline a completely randomized experimental design for the researcher to use.
(c) (6) The turkeys are identified by tags numbered 1 to 30. Use Table B beginning at line 115 to select the turkeys for *one* of the treatments.

**2** (18 points) The salary schedule for teachers in a midwest school district has five steps. Here are the salaries and number of teachers for each step.

| Step | Salary | Teachers |
|---|---|---|
| 1 | \$25,000 | 42 |
| 2 | \$28,000 | 98 |
| 3 | \$35,000 | 138 |
| 4 | \$45,000 | 84 |
| 5 | \$55,000 | 38 |
| | Total | 400 |

(a) (7) Choose a teacher at random from this school district and let $X$ be his or her salary. Give the probability distribution of $X$.
(b) (3) What is the probability that a randomly chosen teacher earns more than \$40,000?
(c) (4) What is the mean salary $\mu_X$ in the school district?
(d) (4) A teacher's contribution to the school district's retirement plan is \$500 plus 5% of his or her salary. What is the mean contribution?

**3** (12 points) A company receives electrical components from a supplier in large shipments. A random sample of 125 components is drawn from each shipment for inspection. Each component is inspected and classified as "conforms to specifications" or "does not conform." The shipment is accepted if no more than 5 of the 125 fail the inspection. Suppose that in fact 8% of the components in a shipment fail to conform to the specifications. What is the probability that the shipment will be accepted?

**4** (12 points) The company in Problem 3 considers a different system for deciding whether to accept or reject a shipment of components. The random sample of 125 components is drawn, and a critical voltage is measured on each one. The shipment is accepted if the average $\overline{x}$ of these voltages is between 348 and 352 volts. Suppose that this voltage varies among the components in the shipment with mean 347 volts and standard deviation 4 volts. What is the probability that the shipment is accepted?

# SAMPLE EXAMINATION 2 SOLUTIONS

## PART I ANSWERS

**1** (d) The population is the group that we want information about.

**2** (a)

**3** (c) A statistic is a number that describes the sample.

**4** (b) The possible values of $X$ are 1, 2, 3, and 4. It is not a count of successes in a fixed number of independent trials, so is not binomial.

**5** (b) This is an experiment because treatments are imposed on the subjects. The race of the men is used to divide them into two blocks.

**6** (c) The basic sampling design deals with bias, while variability is controlled by the size of the sample.

**7** (b) By the multiplication rule for independent events, the probability of 4 straight 9's anywhere in the table is $(1/10)^4$.

**8** (d)

**9** (b) Note that (a) is not correct because a proportion near 1/6 can correspond to a count quite far from 1000 of 6000, and that (c) is wrong because of independence.

**10** (d) Both are counts of successes in $n$ independent trials; $n$ is 1000 in (a) and 24 in (c). There is no fixed number of trials in (b).

**11** (b) The standard deviation of a sample mean $\overline{x}$ is $\sigma/\sqrt{n}$, which is $2/\sqrt{5} = .89$. This fact is true whether or not the distribution is normal.

**12** (a) By the complement rule, the probability that $A$ does *not* work is 0.1 and the probability that $B$ does not work is 0.2. So by the multiplication rule for independent events, the probability that $A$ does not work *and* $B$ does not work is $(.1)(.2) = .02$.

**13** (c) The number of times $X$ that you win has the $B(5, .05)$ distribution. The probability of winning at least once is

$$P(X \geq 1) = 1 - P(X = 0)$$

and from Table C, $P(X = 0) = .7738$.

**14** (b)

**15** (a) Note that the correlation makes no sense for categorical variables.

**16** (d) In the *long run*, about 1/3 will be unlisted.

**17** (b) This is the complement of $A$.

**18** (c)

**19** (b) If $X$ is the weight in pounds, then the weight in kilograms is $X/2.2$ or $.45X$ and so the mean is $\mu_X/2.2$ or $.45\mu_X$ by the rules for means.

**20** (a) The rules for variances and standard deviations say that the standard deviation of $.45X$ is $.45\sigma_X$.

## PART II ANSWERS

**1** (a) There are two factors (independent variables) in the experiment: level of selenium and level of vitamin E. The combinations of levels of these factors give six different diets as shown in the table below. These are the treatments. (All other aspects of the diet, including the dose of salinomycin, are identical in all six diets.)

| | $E_1$ | $E_2$ | $E_3$ |
|---|---|---|---|
| $S_1$ | 1 | 2 | 3 |
| $S_2$ | 4 | 5 | 6 |

(b) A completely randomized design allocates the 30 turkeys at random among all six treatments. Each diet is fed to 5 birds.

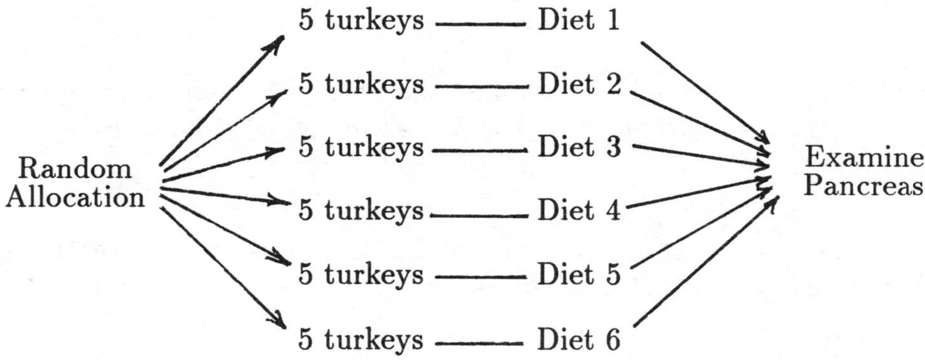


(c) Label the turkeys 01 to 30 (00 to 29 is also acceptable, but be sure that each label has two digits). Read two-digit groups from line 115 of Table B until 5 turkeys are chosen to make up the first group. Those chosen have labels 04, 17, 22, 09, and 26.

**2** (a) Each teacher is equally likely to be chosen, so each has probability 1/400. The probability that the teacher chosen earns $25,000 is then

$$\frac{42}{400} = 0.105$$

because 42 of the 400 teachers earn that amount. The probability distribution found in this way is (salaries in thousands):

| Salary | 25 | 28 | 35 | 45 | 55 |
|---|---|---|---|---|---|
| Probability | .105 | .245 | .345 | .210 | .095 |

Check that the probabilities add to 1.
(b) The probability of any event for this discrete distribution is the sum

of the probabilities of the outcomes that make up the event. So

$$\begin{aligned} P(X > \$40,000) &= P(X = \$45,000) + P(X = \$55,000) \\ &= .210 + .095 = .305 \end{aligned}$$

(c) Use Equation (4.3) of the text to find the mean of a discrete random variable.

$$\begin{aligned} \mu_X &= x_1p_1 + x_2p_2 + \cdots + x_kp_k \\ &= (25)(.105) + (28)(.245) + \cdots + (55)(.095) \\ &= 36.325 \end{aligned}$$

The outcomes are in thousands, so the mean salary is $\mu_X = \$36,235$.
(d) Because 5% is 0.05, the contribution is $500 + 0.05X$. By the rules (4.4) of the text for combining means, the mean contribution is

$$500 + 0.05\mu_X = 500 + (.05)(36,235) = \$2,311.75$$

**3** Because the shipment is large, we can take the 125 items in the sample to be independent of each other. Each has probability 0.08 of failing inspection. The number $X$ that fail is the count of "successes" in 125 independent trials with probability 0.08 of a success on each trial. That is, $X$ has the binomial distribution with $n = 125$ and $p = 0.08$. To calculate a probability for this distribution, we use the normal approximation. The mean and standard deviation of $X$ are

$$\begin{aligned} \mu_X &= np = (125)(.08) = 10 \\ \sigma_X &= \sqrt{np(1-p)} = \sqrt{(125)(.08)(.92)} = 3.033 \end{aligned}$$

The normal approximation says that $X$ has the $N(10, 3.033)$ distribution. The probability that the shipment is accepted is the probability that no more than 5 nonconforming items are found. The result is

$$\begin{aligned} P(X \leq 5) &= P\left(\frac{X-10}{3.033} \leq \frac{5-10}{3.033}\right) \\ &= P(Z \leq -1.65) = 0.0495 \end{aligned}$$

Over 95% of all shipments with 8% bad components will be rejected.

**4** The shipment is accepted if $348 \leq \bar{x} \leq 352$, where $\bar{x}$ is the mean voltage from $n = 125$ components. The central limit theorem says that the distribution of $\bar{x}$ is approximately normal. Its mean and standard deviation are

$$\begin{aligned} \mu_{\bar{x}} &= \mu = 347 \\ \sigma_{\bar{x}} &= \frac{\sigma}{\sqrt{n}} = \frac{4}{\sqrt{125}} = 0.3578 \end{aligned}$$

The probability we want is therefore

$$\begin{aligned} P(348 \leq \bar{x} \leq 352) &= P\left(\frac{348-347}{.3578} \leq Z \leq \frac{352-347}{.3578}\right) \\ &= P(2.79 \leq Z \leq 13.97) \\ &= 1 - .9974 = 0.0026 \end{aligned}$$

Such a shipment will very rarely be accepted. Notice that when a $z$ falls above the range of Table A, we know that the probability below it is 1 to many decimal places.

# UNIT 19
# CONFIDENCE INTERVALS

## LESSON OVERVIEW

Units 19 through 25 are devoted to formal statistical inference. Formal inference attaches a probability statement to its conclusions to indicate how reliable they are. There are two important types of inference, tests of significance and confidence intervals. This unit introduces the basic ideas of **confidence intervals** and their interpretation in a simple setting. Later units will give specific confidence intervals for use in more realistic situations.

A 95% confidence interval for a parameter, such as the mean $\mu$ of a population, is an interval computed from the data that contains the unknown true value of $\mu$ in 95% of all possible samples from the population. The confidence statement has two parts, the interval itself and the **level of confidence**. The level of confidence is usually chosen to be 90%, 95%, or 99%. The text denotes the confidence level by $C$. The confidence level states the probability that the method will give a correct answer. That is, if you use 95% confidence intervals often, in the long run 95% of your intervals will contain the true parameter value. You cannot know whether the result of applying a confidence interval to a particular set of data is correct. The video program points out that confidence intervals lie behind the "margin of error" that news reports often attach to opinion poll results.

In this unit we consider confidence intervals for the mean $\mu$ of a population. We assume that the population is normally distributed and that we have an SRS of size $n$ from the population. These assumptions are often true in practice. We also assume that we know the standard deviation $\sigma$ of the population. This is not realistic, but we want to illustrate the ideas of inference in a simple case. You will learn in Unit 21 what to do when $\sigma$ is not known. The video program looks at testing batteries, such as those used in heart pacemakers, to estimate their mean lifetime quite closely. The standard deviation is of course not known, but the ideas of confidence intervals apply nonetheless.

A level $C$ confidence interval for the mean $\mu$ of a normal population with known standard deviation $\sigma$, based on an SRS of size $n$, is given by

$$\overline{x} \pm z^* \frac{\sigma}{\sqrt{n}}$$

Like many confidence intervals, this has the form

$$\text{estimate} \pm \text{margin of error}$$

The estimate of the unknown $\mu$ is the sample mean $\overline{x}$. The term following the plus-or-minus sign is the margin of error; $z^*$ is the **upper normal critical value** for $C$, given in Table D in the text. This is the point on the standard normal curve with area 0.95 between $-z^*$ and $z^*$. For a 95% confidence interval, for example, we look up the point $z^*$ for $C = 95\%$.

The margin of error of a confidence interval shows how accurate our estimate is. Small margins of error are desirable. Other things being equal, the margin of error of a confidence interval decreases as

- the confidence level $C$ decreases
- the sample size $n$ increases
- the population standard deviation $\sigma$ decreases

If we have chosen a confidence level and know the population standard deviation $\sigma$, we can get a confidence interval with any margin of error we want by picking the sample size $n$. The sample size required to obtain a confidence interval with margin of error $m$ for a normal mean is

$$n = \left(\frac{z^*\sigma}{m}\right)^2$$

where $z^*$ is the critical point for the desired level of confidence. In practice, extra observations can be expensive or impractical. The video visits a primate research center, where monkeys and other primates for use in research are housed. The task of deciding how many primates to use in a medical study is difficult both for ethical reasons and because of the expense involved.

A particular form of confidence interval is correct only under specific conditions. The most important conditions concern the method used to produce the data. Other factors such as the form of the population distribution may also be important.

**Note**: The summary above uses the notation of the text, which is slightly simpler than that of the video. The video uses $1 - \alpha$ for the confidence level, rather than simply $C$. The video also discusses the widths of confidence intervals rather than their margins of error. The width is just two times the margin of error.

## ASSIGNMENT

1. Read the LEARNING OBJECTIVES to see what specific skills you must acquire from this unit.

2. Read Section 6.1 of the text.

3. Do the following problems from the SECTION 6.1 EXERCISES in the text: 6.1, 6.5, 6.7, 6.11, 6.14.

4. Finally, try the SELF-TEST QUESTIONS and compare your answers with those given.

## LEARNING OBJECTIVES

A. State in nontechnical language what is meant by "95% confidence" or other statements of confidence in statistical reports.

B. Calculate a confidence interval for the mean $\mu$ of a normal population with known standard deviation $\sigma$.

C. Recognize when this confidence interval recipe is appropriate, and when the sample design or a small sample from a skewed population make it inappropriate.

D. Understand how the margin of error of a confidence interval changes with the sample size and the level of confidence.

E. Find the sample size required to obtain a confidence interval of specified margin of error $m$ when the confidence level and other information are given.

## SELF-TEST QUESTIONS

**19.1** The report of a sample survey of 1500 adults says, "With 95% confidence, between 27% and 33% of all American adults believe that drugs are the most serious problem facing our nation's public schools." Explain to someone who knows no statistics what the phrase "95% confidence" means in this report.

**19.2** When an instrument in a chemistry laboratory makes repeated measurements on the same specimen, the readings are known to vary normally with standard deviation $\sigma = 0.03$. It is customary to make 3 readings and use the sample mean as the final result. For a particular specimen, the readings are

53.12 53.08 53.17

Give a 95% confidence interval for the mean of the distribution of readings for this specimen. (This mean is the true value being measured if the instrument has no bias.)

**19.3** How many readings made with the instrument in Problem 19.2 must be averaged to obtain a margin of error of $\pm 0.01$ in a 95% confidence interval for the true value?

**19.4** The salaries (in thousands of dollars) of a random sample of 10 of the 380 full professors at a large university are

73, 62, 68, 112, 54, 59, 93, 84, 43, 76

The $z$ or similar procedures should *not* be used to give a confidence interval for the mean salary of a full professor at this university. Why not?

## SELF-TEST SOLUTIONS

**19.1** The phrase "95% confidence" means that we got our result by a method that gives a correct result in 95% of all sample surveys. (The result is the interval 27% to 33% within which the survey estimates the truth about the population to lie. The confidence level tells us how trustworthy this result is. A method that is correct 95% of the time is more trustworthy than one that is correct only 80% of the time.)

**19.2** Calculate that

$$\begin{aligned} \overline{x} &= \frac{\sum x}{n} \\ &= \frac{159.37}{3} = 53.12 \end{aligned}$$

The 95% confidence interval is

$$\begin{aligned} \overline{x} \pm z^* \frac{\sigma}{\sqrt{n}} &= 53.12 \pm 1.960 \frac{0.03}{\sqrt{3}} \\ &= 53.12 \pm 0.034 \end{aligned}$$

or 53.086 to 53.154. The 95% confidence interval used the 0.025 upper critical value $z^*$ of the standard normal distribution, found in Table D.

**19.3** The desired margin of error is $m = 0.01$. We know that $\sigma = 0.03$ and that for 95% confidence $z^* = 1.960$. So

$$\begin{aligned} n &= \left(\frac{z^*\sigma}{m}\right)^2 \\ &= \left(\frac{(1.96)(.03)}{0.01}\right)^2 = 34.6 \end{aligned}$$

We round this result up to $n = 35$. You can see that this is approximately correct by noting that $n = 3$ gave a margin of error of $\pm.03$. A margin of error one-third this requires nine times as many observations ($n = 36$) because the margin of error goes down as the square root of $n$.

**19.4** The salary data contain an outlier (at $112,000) that will strongly affect the sample mean $\overline{x}$. Confidence levels from the normal distribution are not accurate when the distribution is strongly skewed or has outliers unless the sample is quite large. (You should also ask whether the median faculty salary would be more informative than the mean. We will not learn how to give confidence intervals for the median of a population, but it is not difficult.)

# UNIT 20
# SIGNIFICANCE TESTS

## LESSON OVERVIEW

The previous unit introduced the idea of a confidence interval for estimating a population parameter. This unit presents **significance tests** that assess the strength of the evidence for the presence of an effect but do not estimate the size of the effect. The specific test used to explain the ideas applies to the same setting as the confidence interval in Unit 19.

A test begins with a **null hypothesis** $H_0$ that states that the effect sought is *not* present. An **alternative hypothesis** $H_a$ says what effect is being sought. In this unit, hypotheses concern the mean $\mu$ of a population. For example, if we suspect that the body temperature of an ill person is higher than the normal 98.6°F, the null hypothesis says that the mean temperature is normal (no effect),

$$H_0 : \mu = 98.6$$

and the alternative says that it is higher than normal,

$$H_a : \mu > 98.6$$

The hypotheses are always stated in terms of population parameters. Usually $H_0$ says that a parameter takes a fixed value and $H_a$ says that the parameter differs from its null value, in a specific direction (**one-sided alternative**) or in either direction (**two-sided alternative**).

A test of significance is intended to assess the evidence provided by data against a null hypothesis $H_0$ in favor of an alternative hypothesis $H_a$. The video program shows an unusual application of this reasoning in which $H_0$ is the hypothesis that a newly discovered poem was written by Shakespeare and $H_a$ the alternative that the poem is not Shakespeare's work. Statistical tests can only attempt to find evidence against $H_0$. In this case, tests based on word usage fail to give evidence against Shakespeare's authorship: the poem fits his style. Significance tests often appear in courts of law, as the video also illustrates. In a discrimination case, for example, $H_0$ says that there is no difference in the treatment of the protected group and others (no discrimination), while $H_a$ says that there *is* a difference.

A significance test is based on a **test statistic**. The $P$**-value** is the probability, computed assuming that $H_0$ is true, that the test statistic would take a value at least as extreme as that actually observed. Small $P$-values indicate strong evidence against $H_0$. So a significance test asks, "Is the observed outcome likely to occur just by chance if $H_0$ is really true." Unlikely outcomes are evidence against $H_0$.

When the hypotheses concern the mean $\mu$ of a population, the test statistic is the sample mean $\overline{x}$. The $P$-value is the probability that $\overline{x}$ is at least as far from the hypothesized value $\mu_0$ of $\mu$ as the actually observed $\overline{x}$, assuming that the null hypothesis is true. What counts as "far from $\mu_0$" is determined by the alternative hypothesis. If $H_a$ is one-sided, only one direction gives evidence against $H_0$ in favor of $H_a$. If $H_a$ is two-sided, values of $\overline{x}$ far from $\mu_0$ in either direction are evidence against $H_0$.

Calculating $P$-values requires that we know the sampling distribution of the test statistic when $H_0$ is true. To calculate probabilities concerning the sample mean $\overline{x}$, we standardize it. So significance tests for the hypothesis $H_0 : \mu = \mu_0$ concerning the unknown mean $\mu$ of a population are based on the $z$ **statistic**

$$z = \frac{\overline{x} - \mu_0}{\sigma/\sqrt{n}}$$

The statistic $z$ is just $\overline{x}$ standardized. The $z$ test assumes an SRS of size $n$, known population standard deviation $\sigma$, and either a normal population or a large sample. The assumption that $\sigma$ is known is not realistic. Unit 21 will show what to do when $\sigma$ is not known. $P$-values for the $z$ test are computed from the normal distribution (Table A in the text).

If the $P$-value is as small or smaller than a specified value $\alpha$, the data are **statistically significant** at significance level $\alpha$. Fixed $\alpha$ tests based on the $z$ statistic compare $z$ to **standard normal critical values** found in Table D in the text. $P$-values are more informative than the yes-or-no result of a fixed $\alpha$ test. Beware of placing too much weight on traditional values of $\alpha$ such as $\alpha = 0.05$.

The reasoning of significance tests is subtle, and the tests are easily misunderstood. Remember that the $P$-value only tells you if there is good evidence for *some* effect, not whether the effect is large or practically important. Very small effects can be highly significant (small $P$), especially when a test is based on a large sample. A statistically significant effect need not be practically significant. Plot the data to display the effect you are seeking, and use confidence intervals to estimate the actual value of parameters. On the other hand, lack of significance does not imply that $H_0$ is true, especially when the test is based on only a few observations.

Like confidence intervals, the common significance tests are not always valid. Faulty data collection, outliers in the data, and testing a hypothesis on the same data that suggested the hypothesis can invalidate a test. Many tests run at once will probably produce some significant results by chance alone, even if all the null hypotheses are true.

## ASSIGNMENT

1. Read the LEARNING OBJECTIVES to see what specific skills you must acquire from this unit.

2. Read Section 6.2 of the text, and Section 6.3 up to the heading "Power."

3. Do the following problems from the SECTION 6.2 EXERCISES in the text: 6.21, 6.25, 6.27, 6.29, 6.33, 6.35; and the following problems from the SECTION 6.3 EXERCISES: 6.45, 6.47.

4. Finally, try the SELF-TEST QUESTIONS and compare your answers with those given.

## LEARNING OBJECTIVES

A. State appropriate null and alternative hypotheses for a test, particularly when the parameter in question is a population mean $\mu$.

B. Explain in nontechnical language the meaning of the $P$-value when the numerical value of $P$ is given for a specific test.

C. Calculate the $z$ statistic and the $P$-value for both one-sided and two-sided tests about the mean $\mu$ of a normal population.

D. Assess statistical significance at standard levels $\alpha$ either by comparing $P$ to $\alpha$ or by comparing $z$ to standard normal critical values.

E. Recognize that significance testing does not measure the size or importance of an effect.

F. Recognize when the $z$ test is appropriate, and when the data collection design or a small sample from a skewed population make it inappropriate.

## SELF-TEST QUESTIONS

**20.1** Give a brief answer to each of the following questions.
(a) What is the number such that exactly 1% of the probability in a standard normal distribution falls above it?
(b) A chemical production process has had mean output $\mu = 1100$ pounds of product per shift. New pollution controls have been added to the process. Management wants to know if there is evidence that the new controls have reduced production. What are $H_0$ and $H_a$?
(c) The potency of a pharmaceutical product is supposed to be 78. Three potency measurements are taken from each batch produced to

check whether the potency has deviated from the desired level. What are $H_0$ and $H_a$ for this test?
(d) If a statistical test is significant at the 1% level ($\alpha = 0.01$), is the same test using the same data always significant at the 5% level ($\alpha = 0.05$)?

**20.2** You read an article that describes a study of the voting patterns of various groups in society based on a large sample survey. The article says, "Persons who identified themselves as evangelicals were significantly ($P < .01$) more likely to favor Republican presidential candidates than were other white Protestants." Explain to someone who knows no statistics what "significantly ($P < .01$)" means here.

**20.3** The diastolic blood pressure for American women aged 18 to 44 has the normal distribution with mean $\mu = 75$ millimeters of mercury (mm Hg) and standard deviation $\sigma = 10$ mm Hg. We suspect that regular exercise will lower the blood pressure. A sample of 25 women who jog at least 5 miles a week gives sample mean blood pressure $\overline{x} = 71$ mm Hg. Is this good evidence that the mean blood diastolic blood pressure for the population of regular exercisers is lower than 75 mm Hg?
(a) State $H_0$ and $H_a$.
(b) Carry out the test, assuming that $\sigma = 10$ is true. Use Table A to give the $P$-value.
(c) Is the result of your test significant at the 5% level? Is it significant at the 1% level?

**20.4** A milling machine produces rods that are supposed to be 5 centimeters (cm) in diameter. When the machine is in control, the rod diameters vary normally with mean $\mu = 5$ cm and standard deviation $\sigma = 0.002$ cm. The standard deviation measures the precision of the milling machine. A sample of 5 rods is measured each hour for process control purposes. This hour's sample gives

5.0009   5.0007   5.0010   5.0009   5.0010

Is there evidence that the process mean has moved away from the target value? Answer this question by stating hypotheses and carrying out a significance test. Give the $P$-value and state your conclusion.

## SELF-TEST SOLUTIONS

**20.1** (a) Table D gives the value $z^*$ having probability $p = 0.01$ above it for the standard normal distribution as $z^* = 2.326$
(b) We ask if there is evidence that the mean has *decreased* from its "no effect" value of 1100 pounds, a one-sided alternative. So

$$H_0 : \mu = 1100$$

$$H_a : \mu < 1100$$

(c) We ask if there is evidence that the mean potency has *changed* from its target value of 78, a two-sided alternative. So if $\mu$ is the mean of the population of potency measurements,

$$H_0 : \mu = 78$$

$$H_a : \mu \neq 78$$

(d) Yes. For the test to be significant at the 1% level, the test statistic must fall in the extreme 1% of its values. This means that it is also in the extreme 5% and is therefore significant at the 5% level. In other words, a result so extreme that it occurs in less than 1% of all cases when $H_0$ is true certainly occurs in less than 5% of all cases.

**20.2** Evangelicals in the sample favored the Republican candidate more often than did other white Protestants. Some difference would occur by chance in a random sample even if the two groups as a whole held the same opinion. But the difference the survey found is so large that it would rarely occur just by chance. That's what we mean by calling it "significant." The "$P < .01$" says that a difference this large would occur in less than 1% of all samples if evangelicals really did not differ from other white protestants.

**20.3** (a) The alternative is one-sided because we suspect that exercisers have *lower* blood pressure.

$$H_0 : \mu = 75$$
$$H_a : \mu < 75$$

(b) The $z$ statistic is

$$\begin{aligned} z &= \frac{\overline{x} - \mu_0}{\sigma/\sqrt{n}} \\ &= \frac{71 - 75}{10/\sqrt{25}} = -2.00 \end{aligned}$$

The $P$-value is the probability that $z$ takes a value this small or smaller. Because $z$ has the standard normal distribution when $H_0$ is true, this is $P(Z \leq -2.00)$. From Table A, $P = 0.0228$.
(c) The result is significant at level $\alpha$ if $P \leq \alpha$. In this case the result *is* significant at the 5% level ($\alpha = .05$), but is *not* significant at the 1% level ($\alpha = .01$).

**20.4** The hypotheses concern the mean rod diameter $\mu$. We are interested in detecting a deviation from the target diameter (5 cm) in either direction. So

$$H_0 : \mu = 5$$

$$H_a : \mu \neq 5$$

The sample mean of the 5 rods measured is

$$\overline{x} = \frac{\sum x}{n} = \frac{25.0045}{5} = 5.0009$$

The $z$ statistic is

$$\begin{aligned} z &= \frac{\overline{x} - \mu_0}{\sigma/\sqrt{n}} \\ &= \frac{5.0009 - 5}{0.002/\sqrt{5}} = 1.006 \end{aligned}$$

The $P$-value for a two-sided test is the probability that $z$ takes a value at least this far from 0 in either direction. Because the standard normal distribution is symmetric about 0, we can just find $P(Z \geq 1.006)$ and double it. From Table A, rounding 1.006 to 1.01,

$$P(Z \geq 1.01) = 1 - .8438 = 0.1562$$

The $P$-value is therefore double this, or about 0.31. A value of $\overline{x}$ as far from 5 as that observed will occur in 31% of all samples when the process is in control with $\mu = 5$. There is no reason to think that $\mu$ has moved away from its target of 5 cm.

# UNIT 21
# INFERENCE FOR ONE MEAN

## LESSON OVERVIEW

This unit presents both confidence intervals and significance tests for the common situation in which we want to make an inference about the mean $\mu$ of a population. This situation is the same as that of Units 19 and 20, except that now the population standard deviation $\sigma$ is also unknown. The most important idea of this unit is to replace the unknown $\sigma$ by the sample standard deviation $s$ in the $z$ procedures described in Units 19 and 20. This substitution changes the $z$ procedures into $t$ **procedures** for inference. Both the confidence interval and significance test are carried out as in the earlier units, but a table of a new distribution, the $t$ **distribution**, must be used in place of the standard normal tables.

There are several kinds of $t$ statistics, all of which have $t$ distributions. We will meet other $t$ statistics in later units. There is a family of $t$ distributions, one for each number of **degrees of freedom**. The degrees of freedom are related to the number of observations used in a $t$ statistic. All $t$ distributions are continuous and have symmetric density curves similar in shape to the standard normal density curve. The $t$ distributions approach the standard normal distribution as the number of degrees of freedom gets larger.

Recall that the standardized sample mean, or **one-sample $z$ statistic,**

$$z = \frac{\overline{x} - \mu}{\sigma/\sqrt{n}}$$

has the $N(0,1)$ distribution. If the standard deviation $\sigma/\sqrt{n}$ of $\overline{x}$ is replaced by the **standard error** $s/\sqrt{n}$, the result is the **one-sample $t$ statistic**

$$t = \frac{\overline{x} - \mu}{s/\sqrt{n}}$$

This statistic has the $t$ distribution with $n-1$ degrees of freedom. An exact level $C$ confidence interval for the mean $\mu$ of a normal population is

$$\overline{x} \pm t^* \frac{s}{\sqrt{n}}$$

where $t^*$ is the upper $(1-C)/2$ critical value of the $t(n-1)$ distribution. Critical values of the $t$ distributions are given in Table E in the text. Significance tests for $H_0 : \mu = \mu_0$ are based on the $t$ statistic. $P$-values or fixed significance levels are computed from the $t(n-1)$ distribution.

The same $t$ procedures that are used for inference about a single population mean $\mu$ also apply to **matched pairs** data, that is, to data that are before-and-after observations on the same subject or otherwise matched in pairs. Just take the difference within each matched pair to produce a single sample and then use the $t$ procedures. The video contains two examples of matched pairs designs. The first is a taste test to determine if a new cola loses sweetness in storage. The pairs in this setting are before-and-after taste scores from the same taster. The second example studies scores of autistic children on two measures of development; the pairs are scores from the same child.

The $t$ tests and confidence intervals assume that the population is normally distributed. Because of the central limit theorem, these procedures are approximately correct for other population distributions when the sample is large. The $t$ procedures are relatively **robust** against nonnormal populations, especially for larger sample sizes. The $t$ procedures are useful for nonnormal data when $n \geq 15$ unless the data show outliers or strong skewness.

## ASSIGNMENT

1. Read the LEARNING OBJECTIVES to see what specific skills you must acquire from this unit.

2. Read Section 7.1 of the text, omitting the starred optional material at the end of the section.

3. Do the following problems from the SECTION 7.1 EXERCISES in the text: 7.1, 7.3, 7.7, 7.9, 7.18.

4. Finally, try the SELF-TEST QUESTIONS and compare your answers with those given.

## LEARNING OBJECTIVES

A. Use the $t$ procedure to obtain a confidence interval at a stated level of confidence for the mean $\mu$ of a population.

B. Carry out a $t$ test for the hypothesis that a population mean $\mu$ has a specified value against either a one-sided or a two-sided alternative. Use the table of $t$ critical values to approximate the $P$-value or carry out a fixed-$\alpha$ test.

C. Recognize when the $t$ procedures are appropriate in practice, and also when the data collection design or a small sample from a skewed distribution makes them inappropriate.

D. Recognize matched pairs data and use the $t$ procedures to carry out confidence intervals and tests of significance for such data.

## SELF-TEST QUESTIONS

**21.1** Give brief answers to each of the following questions.
(a) What is the number $t^*$ with exactly probability 0.025 falling above it in the $t$ distribution with 10 degrees of freedom?
(b) What critical value $t^*$ would you use in a 90% one-sample $t$ confidence interval based on 20 observations?
(c) The one-sample $t$ statistic based on 15 observations takes the value $t = 3$. Between what two levels from Table E does the $P$-value lie if the test is one-sided?
(d) Between what two levels does the $P$-value of the $t$ statistic in (c) lie if the test is two-sided?

**21.2** A milk processor monitors the number of bacteria per milliliter in raw milk received for processing. A random sample of 10 one-milliliter specimens from milk supplied by one producer gives the following data:

5370, 4890, 5100, 4500, 5260, 5150, 4900, 4760, 4700, 4870

(a) Give a 90% confidence interval for the mean bacteria count per milliliter in this producer's milk.
(b) What assumptions are required by the method you used in (a)? How would you verify these assumptions? (You need not actually attempt to verify the assumptions.)

**21.3** The amount of wax deposited on the outside surface of waxed paper bags during production may vary from the amount deposited on the inside surface. A sample of 25 bags is measured. For each bag, the wax concentration in pounds per square foot is determined on the inside and outside. The difference (outside minus inside) is calculated for each bag. The mean and standard deviation of these 25 differences are

$$\overline{x} = 0.093 \quad s = 0.723$$

Is there good evidence that the mean concentrations on the two surfaces are not equal?

**21.4** The reaction times of subjects to a stimulus in an experiment on visual perception are not normally distributed. A few very slow reactions give the distribution a long right tail. The experimental psychologist wants to determine whether the mean reaction time is less than 5 milliseconds based on 8 observations. Should she use a $t$ test? Explain your answer.

## SELF-TEST SOLUTIONS

**21.1** (a) Table E for $df = 10$ and $p = .025$ gives $t^* = 2.228$.

(b) Because there are $n = 20$ observations, there are 19 degrees of freedom. Table E with $df = 19$ and $C = 90\%$ gives $t^* = 1.729$.
(c) Because there are $n = 15$ observations, the $t$ statistic has 14 degrees of freedom. Look in the $df = 14$ row of Table E; $t = 3$ lies between the entries for 0.005 ($t^* = 2.997$) and for 0.0025 ($t^* = 3.326$). Because the test is one-sided, the $P$-value is the probability above $t = 3$. So $P$ lies between 0.0025 and 0.005.
(d) The $P$-value for a two-sided test is the probability that $t$ takes a value as far from 0 in either direction as the observed $t = 3$. Because the $t$ distributions are symmetric about 0, we can just double the probability that $t$ falls above 3. We saw in (c) that this probability lies between 0.0025 and 0.005. Doubling these, $P$ lies between 0.005 and 0.01.

**21.2** (a) First calculate the mean $\overline{x}$ and the standard deviation $s$ of the sample. You should have a calculator that will obtain these values from keyed-in data. If you are using a basic calculator, proceed as follows:

$$\begin{aligned}
\sum x &= 49,500 \\
\sum x^2 &= 245,673,600 \\
\overline{x} &= \frac{\sum x}{n} = \frac{49,500}{10} = 4950 \\
s^2 &= \frac{1}{n-1}\left(\sum x^2 - \frac{1}{n}\left(\sum x\right)^2\right) \\
&= \frac{1}{9}(245,673,600 - 245,025,000) = 72,066.67 \\
s &= \sqrt{72,066.67} = 268.45
\end{aligned}$$

The 90% confidence interval is

$$\begin{aligned}
\overline{x} \pm t^* \frac{s}{\sqrt{n}} &= 4950 \pm 1.833 \frac{268.45}{\sqrt{10}} \\
&= 4950 \pm 155.6
\end{aligned}$$

This interval uses the critical value from the $t(9)$ distribution for $C =$ 90%, found in Table E.
(b) The two assumptions required are that the data be an SRS from the producer's milk and that the distribution of bacteria counts in the population of milk be approximately normally distributed. You must find out how the sample was chosen to see if it can be regarded as an SRS. A normal quantile plot shows that the distribution is close to normal.

**21.3** This is a matched pairs situation. The inner and outer surface of the same bag are paired with each other. We want to test the hypothesis of "no difference," or

$$H_0 : \mu = 0$$
$$H_a : \mu \neq 0$$

where $\mu$ is the mean of the difference in wax concentrations on the two surfaces. The one-sample $t$ statistic is

$$\begin{aligned} t &= \frac{\overline{x} - \mu_0}{s/\sqrt{n}} \\ &= \frac{0.093 - 0}{0.723/\sqrt{25}} = 0.643 \end{aligned}$$

Compare this value with critical points of the $t(24)$ distribution. Table E shows that $t = 0.643$ is less than the $p = 0.25$ critical value, which is $t^* = 0.685$. Because the test is two-sided, we double the $p$ from the table to get the $P$-value. So $P$ is less than 0.5. There is no evidence that the wax concentrations on the two surfaces differ.

**21.4** No. The $t$ procedures are designed for use with random samples from a normal distribution. For large samples, $t$ procedures are accurate for other distributions because the central limit theorem guarantees that $\overline{x}$ is nearly normal. For moderate sample sizes (say at least 15), $t$

is quite accurate unless the population distribution is strongly skewed or has outliers. The psychologist has a small sample (only 8) from a right-skewed distribution. Procedures based on the $t$ distribution are not accurate in this case.

# UNIT 22
# COMPARING TWO MEANS

## LESSON OVERVIEW

We saw in Unit 12 that comparison of several treatments is one of the principles of good experimental design. This unit discusses tests and confidence intervals for comparing the mean response to two treatments. More generally, these methods apply whenever we want to compare the means $\mu_1$ and $\mu_2$ of two separate populations based on independent observations from each population. The video presents several situations in which we want to compare two means: Does a new welfare system raise the mean income of welfare recipients? Does a new foam for seating differ in mean resilience from standard seating? Does coaching raise mean SAT scores?

To compare the means of Population 1 and Population 2, we can give a confidence interval for the difference $\mu_1 - \mu_2$ between the means, or we can test the hypothesis $H_0 : \mu_1 = \mu_2$ that there is no difference. Tests and confidence intervals for the difference of the means $\mu_1$ and $\mu_2$ of two normal populations are based on the difference $\overline{x}_1 - \overline{x}_2$ of the sample means from two independent SRSs. Because of the central limit theorem, the resulting procedures are approximately correct for other population distributions when the sample sizes are large.

Suppose that we have independent SRSs of sizes $n_1$ and $n_2$ from two normal populations with parameters $\mu_1$, $\sigma_1$ and $\mu_2$, $\sigma_2$. Because $\overline{x}_1 - \overline{x}_2$ has a normal distribution, we can standardize it to obtain a statistic with the $N(0,1)$ distribution. This is the **two-sample $z$ statistic**

$$z = \frac{(\overline{x}_1 - \overline{x}_2) - (\mu_1 - \mu_2)}{\sqrt{\frac{\sigma_1^2}{n_1} + \frac{\sigma_2^2}{n_2}}}$$

Substituting the sample standard deviations $s_1$ and $s_2$ from the two samples changes $z$ into a new $t$ statistic, the **two-sample $t$ statistic**

$$t = \frac{(\overline{x}_1 - \overline{x}_2) - (\mu_1 - \mu_2)}{\sqrt{\frac{s_1^2}{n_1} + \frac{s_2^2}{n_2}}}$$

This $t$ statistic does *not* have exactly a $t$ distribution. But its distribution is close to the $t(k)$ distribution with degrees of freedom $k$ equal to the smaller of $n_1 - 1$ and $n_2 - 1$.

Inference procedures using the two-sample $t$ statistic with the $t(k)$ distribution are always conservative in the sense of claiming less than they actually accomplish. That is, the true confidence level is higher than is claimed and the true $P$-value is lower. We will use these conservative procedures. Most statistical software uses this same $t$ statistic with a more accurate distribution that is not practical for hand calculation.

Here are the specific two-sample $t$ procedures. The confidence interval for $\mu_1 - \mu_2$ given by

$$(\overline{x}_1 - \overline{x}_2) \pm t^* \sqrt{\frac{s_1^2}{n_1} + \frac{s_2^2}{n_2}}$$

has confidence level at least $C$ if $t^*$ is the upper $(1 - C)/2$ critical value for $t(k)$ with $k$ the smaller of $n_1 - 1$ and $n_2 - 1$. Significance tests for $H_0 : \mu_1 = \mu_2$ based on

$$t = \frac{\overline{x}_1 - \overline{x}_2}{\sqrt{\frac{s_1^2}{n_1} + \frac{s_2^2}{n_2}}}$$

have a true $P$-value no lower than that calculated from $t(k)$.

The guidelines for practical use of two-sample $t$ procedures are similar to those for one-sample $t$ procedures. Equal sample sizes are recommended. We may also be interested in comparing not the mean (center) but the standard deviation (spread) of two populations. There are inference procedures that do this when the populations are normal. But these procedures, unlike the $t$ procedures for means, are extremely sensitive to deviations from normality. We therefore recommend that you avoid inference about standard deviations.

## ASSIGNMENT

1. Read the LEARNING OBJECTIVES to see what specific skills you must acquire from this unit.

2. Read Section 7.2 of the text, omitting the starred optional material at the end. Also read the introduction to Section 7.3, stopping at the heading "The F test."

3. Do the following problem from the SECTION 7.1 EXERCISES in the text: 7.24; and the following problems from the SECTION 7.2 EXERCISES: 7.35, 7.37, 7.45.

4. Finally, try the SELF-TEST QUESTIONS and compare your answers with those given.

## LEARNING OBJECTIVES

A. Recognize a two-sample problem and be able to distinguish such problems from one-sample and matched pairs situations.

B. Give a confidence interval for the difference between two means, using the two-sample $t$ statistic with conservative degrees of freedom.

C. Test the hypothesis that two populations have equal means against either a one-sided or a two-sided alternative, using the two-sample $t$ test with conservative degrees of freedom.

D. Recognize when the two-sample $t$ procedures are appropriate in practice.

E. Know that procedures for comparing the standard deviations of two normal populations are available, but that these procedures are risky because they are not at all robust against non-normal distributions.

## SELF-TEST QUESTIONS

**22.1** In an experiment to study the effect of the spectrum of the ambient light on the growth of plants, tobacco seedlings were divided at random into two groups of 8 plants each. The plants were grown in a greenhouse under identical conditions except for lighting. The experimental group was grown under blue light, the control group under natural light. Here are the data on stem growth in millimeters.

| Control Group | | Experimental | |
|---|---|---|---|
| 4.3 | 4.2 | 3.1 | 2.9 |
| 3.9 | 4.1 | 3.2 | 3.2 |
| 4.1 | 4.2 | 2.7 | 2.9 |
| 3.8 | 4.1 | 3.0 | 3.1 |

Give a 90% confidence interval for the amount by which blue light reduces stem growth during this period.

**22.2** A study of the effect of eating sweetened cereals on tooth decay in children compared 73 children (Group 1) who ate such cereals regularly with 302 children (Group 2) who did not. After three years the number of new cavities was measured for each child. The summary statistics are:

| Group | $n$ | $\overline{x}$ | $s$ |
|---|---|---|---|
| 1 | 73 | 3.41 | 3.62 |
| 2 | 302 | 2.20 | 2.67 |

(a) The researchers suspected that sweetened cereals increase the mean number of cavities. Is there significant evidence for this suspicion at the 1% level?
(b) Does your result depend heavily on the shape of the distribution of cavity counts? Does it depend heavily on any other fact?

## SELF-TEST SOLUTIONS

**22.1** This is a two-sample situation. Call plants grown under natural light Population 1 and plants grown under blue light Population 2. Calculate the sample means and variances for the two samples separately. If you use a basic calculator, the work is as follows for the control group:

$$\begin{aligned}
\overline{x}_1 &= \frac{32.7}{8} = 4.0875 \\
s_1^2 &= \frac{1}{n_1 - 1}\{\sum x^2 - \frac{1}{n_1}(\sum x)^2\} \\
&= \frac{1}{7}(133.85 - \frac{32.7^2}{8}) = 0.0270
\end{aligned}$$

Similar calculations for the experimental group give $\overline{x}_2 = 3.0125$ and $s_2^2 = 0..0298$. The 90% confidence interval for the difference $\mu_1 - \mu_2$ between the population means is

$$\begin{aligned}
&(\overline{x}_1 - \overline{x}_2) \pm t^* \sqrt{\frac{s_1^2}{n_1} + \frac{s_2^2}{n_2}} \\
&= (4.0875 - 3.0125) \pm 1.895\sqrt{\frac{.0270}{8} + \frac{.0298}{8}} \\
&= 1.075 \pm 0.160 \\
&= (0.915,\ 1.235)
\end{aligned}$$

The degrees of freedom are 7, because both $n_1 - 1$ and $n_2 - 1$ are 7. The confidence interval uses the $C = 90\%$ critical value of the $t(7)$ distribution, which Table E gives as $t^* = 1.895$.

**22.2** (a) This is another two-sample situation. We wish to test the null hypothesis that there is no difference between the groups against the one-sided alternative hypothesis that the mean count of cavities is greater in Group 1,

$$H_0 : \mu_1 = \mu_2$$
$$H_a : \mu_1 > \mu_2$$

The two-sample $t$ test statistic is

$$\begin{aligned} t &= \frac{\overline{x}_1 - \overline{x}_2}{\sqrt{\frac{s_1^2}{n_1} + \frac{s_2^2}{n_2}}} \\ &= \frac{3.41 - 2.20}{\sqrt{\frac{3.62^2}{73} + \frac{2.67^2}{302}}} = 2.68 \end{aligned}$$

To assess the significance of the one-sided test, compare $t = 2.68$ with the upper critical values of the $t(72)$ distribution. The degrees of freedom is the smaller of $n_1 - 1 = 72$ and $n_2 - 1 = 301$. Using the $df = 60$ line in Table E, the 0.01 critical value is $t^* = 2.390$. The observed $t$ is larger than $t^*$, so the result is significant at the 1% level. There is strong evidence that the sweetened cereal group has more cavities on the average.

When the exact degrees of freedom needed does not appear in the table, use the next lower tabled degrees of freedom. These critical values are a little larger than the exactly correct values, so we can be certain that an outcome that is significant using the table value is also significant using the exact value.
(b) Because the samples are both quite large, the sample means $\overline{x}_1$ and $\overline{x}_2$ will have distributions that are close to normal even if the individual cavity counts are not normally distributed. The results do not depend on the shape of the two population distributions.

In order to draw conclusions about the two populations, all children who regularly eat sweetened cereals and all children who do not, the samples in the study must be considered random samples from these populations. This assumption is very important. The researchers must explain how they chose their subjects.

# UNIT 23
# INFERENCE FOR PROPORTIONS

## LESSON OVERVIEW

In this unit we turn from inference about population means to inference about another parameter, the **proportion** or percent of successes in a population. As in our study of the binomial distributions, we use "success" as shorthand for any characteristic we are interested in. In the video, the Bureau of Labor Statistics must estimate the percent of the labor force who are unemployed each month. And an investigation of whether contaminated water caused cancer in Woburn, Massachusetts must test the hypothesis that the proportion of cancer cases is the same among people who did and did not drink the suspect water. The first example concerns a proportion in a single population, while the second compares the proportions of successes in two distinct populations. This unit presents inference methods for both settings.

First, suppose that we have an SRS of size $n$ from a population that contains an unknown proportion $p$ of successes. The count $X$ of successes in the sample has the binomial distribution $B(n, p)$ if the population is much larger than the sample. The sample proportion of successes is

$\hat{p} = X/n$. The normal approximation to the binomial distributions says that $\hat{p}$ has approximately a normal distribution. The statistic used for inference about $p$ is the $z$ **statistic** formed by standardizing $\hat{p}$. This statistic is

$$z = \frac{\hat{p} - p}{\sqrt{\frac{p(1-p)}{n}}}$$

The unknown $p$ in the denominator of $z$ is handled differently in confidence intervals and in tests of significance.

A level $C$ confidence interval for $p$ is given by

$$\hat{p} \pm z^* \sqrt{\frac{\hat{p}(1-\hat{p})}{n}}$$

where $z^*$ is the upper $(1-C)/2$ critical value of the standard normal distribution. Notice that the unknown $p$ in the denominator of $z$ was estimated by $\hat{p}$ to form the confidence interval.

Tests of the hypothesis $H_0 : p = p_0$ are based on the test statistic

$$z = \frac{\hat{p} - p_0}{\sqrt{\frac{p_0(1-p_0)}{n}}}$$

and standard normal critical values. Here the unknown $p$ was replaced by the hypothesized value $p_0$. Because these $z$ procedures are based on the normal approximation to the binomial distributions, they can be used only when the sample is moderately large. A helpful rule of thumb is that both $n\hat{p}$ and $n(1-\hat{p})$ should be 10 or larger.

To compare two population proportions, $p_1$ in Population 1 and $p_2$ in Population 2, we use the difference $D = \hat{p}_1 - \hat{p}_2$ between the proportions of successes in samples from each of the populations. Suppose that both samples are SRSs and that the sample sizes are $n_1$ and $n_2$.

The difference $D$ of sample proportions has approximately the normal distribution with mean

$$\mu_D = p_1 - p_2$$

and standard deviation

$$\sigma_D = \sqrt{\frac{p_1(1-p_1)}{n_1} + \frac{p_2(1-p_2)}{n_2}}$$

Inference procedures for $p_1 - p_2$ are based on standardizing $\hat{p}_1 - \hat{p}_2$ to get a **two-sample $z$ statistic.** Because the null hypothesis that there is no difference between the populations

$$H_0 : p_1 = p_2$$

says that $p_1$ and $p_2$ have a common value, the results of the two samples are combined (or **pooled**) to estimate the proportion in this case. We do not pool when a confidence interval is wanted. Watch out for this difference between the confidence interval and test procedures when you study the details of this unit.

The level $C$ confidence interval for $p_1 - p_2$ is

$$(\hat{p}_1 - \hat{p}_2) \pm z^* s_D$$

where

$$s_D = \sqrt{\frac{\hat{p}_1(1-\hat{p}_1)}{n_1} + \frac{\hat{p}_2(1-\hat{p}_2)}{n_2}}$$

and $z^*$ is the upper $(1 - C)/2$ critical value of the standard normal distribution.

Tests for $H_0 : p_1 = p_2$ are based on the $z$ statistic

$$z = \frac{\hat{p}_1 - \hat{p}_2}{s_p}$$

and standard normal critical values. The denominator of this $z$ is

$$s_p = \sqrt{\hat{p}(1 - \hat{p}) \left( \frac{1}{n_1} + \frac{1}{n_2} \right)}$$

where $\hat{p}$ is the overall proportion of successes in the two samples combined. Once again, these $z$ procedures can be used only when the samples are moderately large.

## ASSIGNMENT

1. Read the LEARNING OBJECTIVES to see what specific skills you must acquire from this unit.

2. Read Sections 8.1 and 8.2 of the text.

3. Do the following problems from the SECTION 8.1 EXERCISES in the text: 8.1, 8.5, 8.9; and the following problems from the SECTION 8.2 EXERCISES: 8.21, 8.25.

4. Finally, try the SELF-TEST QUESTIONS and compare your answers with those given.

## LEARNING OBJECTIVES

A. Recognize when an inference problem concerns a population proportion or comparing two population proportions.

B. Use the $z$ statistic based on the normal approximation to the binomial distributions to carry out a test of significance for the hypothesis $H_0 : p = p_0$ about a population proportion $p$ against either a one-sided or a two-sided alternative.

C. Use the $z$ procedure to give a confidence interval for a population proportion $p$.

D. Use a two-sample $z$ procedure to give a confidence interval for the difference $p_1 - p_2$ between proportions in two populations based on independent samples from the populations.

E. Use a $z$ statistic to test the hypothesis $p_1 = p_2$ that proportions in two distinct populations are equal.

F. Understand that all of these procedures are based on the normal approximation to the binomial distributions and so require moderately large samples.

## SELF-TEST QUESTIONS

**23.1** The Forest Service is considering additional restrictions on the number of vehicles allowed to enter Yellowstone National Park. To assess public reaction, the Service asks a random sample of 150 visitors if they favor the proposal. Of these, 89 say "Yes." Give a 99% confidence interval for the proportion of all visitors to Yellowstone who favor the restrictions. Are you 99% confident that more than half are in favor? Explain your answer.

**23.2** A random sample of students at Upper Wabash Tech is asked whether they favor limiting enrollment in crowded majors as a way of keeping the quality of instruction high. The student government suspects that the plan will be unpopular among freshmen, who have not yet been admitted to a major. Here are the responses for freshmen and seniors.

| | Favor | Oppose |
|---|---|---|
| Freshman | 40 | 160 |
| Seniors | 80 | 20 |

(a) Is there strong evidence that a higher proportion of freshmen than of seniors oppose the plan? Give a $P$-value and state your conclusion.
(b) Give a 95% confidence interval for the difference between the proportion of freshmen who oppose the plan and the proportion of seniors who oppose it.

**23.3** A manufacturer of rocket motors test fires a new model in a stationary test stand. The motor ignites properly on 6 of 7 independent trials. Can you use any procedure we have learned to estimate the long run proportion of firings on which this motor will ignite properly? Explain your answer.

## SELF-TEST SOLUTIONS

**23.1** We want a 99% confidence interval for the proportion $p$ of all current visitors to Yellowstone who favor restrictions on vehicles. The sample proportion is

$$\hat{p} = \frac{89}{150} = 0.593$$

The 99% confidence interval is

$$\begin{aligned} \hat{p} \pm z^* \sqrt{\frac{\hat{p}(1-\hat{p})}{n}} &= 0.593 \pm 2.576\sqrt{\frac{(.593)(.407)}{150}} \\ &= 0.593 \pm 0.103 \end{aligned}$$

or 49.0% to 69.6%. The 99% confidence interval uses the 0.005 upper critical value of the standard normal distribution from Table D. We are not 99% confident that more than half approve, because the interval extends below 0.5.

Notice that $n\hat{p} = 89$ and $n(1-\hat{p}) = 61$ are both much larger than 10, so that the normal distribution is an excellent approximation in this case.

**23.2** Call the freshmen Population 1 and the seniors Population 2. The sample proportions who oppose the plan are

$$\hat{p}_1 = \frac{160}{200} = 0.80$$
$$\hat{p}_2 = \frac{20}{100} = 0.20$$

(a) To calculate the two-sample $z$ test statistic, use the pooled estimate of the proportion of students who oppose the plan,

$$\hat{p} = \frac{160+20}{200+100} = 0.60$$

Then

$$\begin{aligned} s_p &= \sqrt{\hat{p}(1-\hat{p})\left(\frac{1}{n_1}+\frac{1}{n_2}\right)} \\ &= \sqrt{(.6)(.4)\left(\frac{1}{200}+\frac{1}{100}\right)} = 0.06 \end{aligned}$$

$$
\begin{aligned}
z &= \frac{\hat{p}_1 - \hat{p}_2}{s_p} \\
&= \frac{0.8 - 0.2}{0.06} = 10.0
\end{aligned}
$$

We wish to test the hypotheses

$$H_0 : p_1 = p_2$$

$$H_a : p_1 > p_2$$

The $P$-value for the one-sided test is $P(Z > 10)$. This is zero to many decimal places. There is extremely strong evidence that more freshmen than seniors oppose the restrictions.

(b) The 95% confidence interval for $p_1 - p_2$ is

$$(\hat{p}_1 - \hat{p}_2) \pm z^* s_D$$

where $z^* = 1.96$ is the 0.025 standard normal critical value from Table D. Calculate that

$$
\begin{aligned}
s_D &= \sqrt{\frac{\hat{p}_1(1-\hat{p}_1)}{n_1} + \frac{\hat{p}_2(1-\hat{p}_2)}{n_2}} \\
&= \sqrt{\frac{(.8)(.2)}{200} + \frac{(.2)(.8)}{100}} = 0.0490
\end{aligned}
$$

The confidence interval is

$$
\begin{aligned}
(\hat{p}_1 - \hat{p}_2) \pm z^* s_D &= (.8 - .2) \pm (1.96)(.049) \\
&= 0.6 \pm 0.096
\end{aligned}
$$

or 0.504 to 0.696. There is a large difference between the freshman and senior proportions.

**23.3** The observed number of successful ignitions has the binomial distribution $B(n, p)$ where $n = 8$ and we want to estimate $p$. Because $n$ is so small, the normal approximation cannot be used. Our methods for inference about a proportion $p$ are all based on the normal approximation, so they do not apply to this problem. (There are methods that use the exact binomial distribution, but we will not study them.)

# UNIT 24
# INFERENCE FOR TWO-WAY TABLES

## LESSON OVERVIEW

The relation between two ways of classifying people or things is displayed by a **two-way table** of counts. This unit concerns inference about two-way tables. You may want to review two-way tables from Unit 11 before studying this unit. A two-way table can compare the distributions of a categorical variable in several populations. The video compares counts of different wear marks on fossil teeth from two species of prehistoric humans. The type of wear mark is the categorical variable, and the two species are two populations. A two-way table can also display data on the relation between two categorical variables in a single population. The video examines the relation between the age of a breast cancer patient and the treatment she receives. Treatment is a categorical variable, and we make age categorical by grouping the patients as "older women" and "younger women."

The simplest two-way table compares the counts of successes and failures in samples from two populations. In the previous unit, we used a two-sample $z$ statistic to test whether the proportions of successes in two populations are equal. The test we will learn in this unit gives the same result as the two-sample $z$ test when two proportions are being compared, but it also applies much more generally.

The overall question asked in this unit is whether or not there is an relationship between two ways of classifying a case (that is, a person or thing). For example, is there a relationship between the age (younger or older) of a woman and the type of breast cancer treatment she receives (three types)? The data are displayed in a two-way table that shows the counts for all six combinations of age and treatment. The null hypothesis says that there is no relationship between age and treatment. The exact statement of $H_0$ can be complex, as an optional section in the text explains in detail. Fortunately, the **chi-square test** for the hypothesis of "no relationship" is quite simple.

Suppose then that we have a two-way table of counts. If the table has $r$ rows and $c$ columns, it is called an $r \times c$ table. The **table total** is the sum $n$ of all the counts in the table. The table total is the total number of cases on which we have data. To test the hypothesis $H_0$ of "no relationship," first write the sums of all counts in each row at the right of the table as **row totals** and the sums of all entries in each column at the bottom of the table as **column totals**. If the null hypothesis is true, the **expected count** in each position is

$$\text{expected count} = \frac{\text{row total} \times \text{column total}}{n}$$

The **chi-square statistic** is

$$X^2 = \sum \frac{(\text{observed count} - \text{expected count})^2}{\text{expected count}}$$

Large values of $X^2$ show that the counts are far from the values they are expected to have if $H_0$ is true. This is evidence against $H_0$ in favor of the alternative that there is association present.

To carry out the significance test, the value of the statistic $X^2$ is compared with critical values of the **chi-square distribution** with $(r-1)(c-1)$ degrees of freedom. These values are given in Table G in the text. The chi-square distributions are a new type of distribution. There is a different chi-square distribution for each number of degrees of freedom. The chi-square distributions are not symmetric like the normal and $t$ distributions, but are skewed to the right.

Remember that the chi-square test does not say whether the association is large or practically important, only whether an association this large is likely to occur by chance alone. To show the size of the association, calculate and compare several percents as you did in Unit 11.

## ASSIGNMENT

1. Read the LEARNING OBJECTIVES to see what specific skills you must acquire from this unit.

2. Read Section 8.3 of the text up to the optional starred subsection entitled "Models for Two-Way Tables."

3. Do the following problems from the SECTION 8.3 EXERCISES in the text: 8.35, 8.39.

4. Finally, try the SELF-TEST QUESTIONS and compare your answers with those given.

# LEARNING OBJECTIVES

A. Arrange counts comparing outcomes in several populations, or counts of items classified by two kinds of outcomes, in a two-way table. Describe the differences among populations or the association between variables by comparing appropriate percents.

B. Recognize when an inference question can be formulated as testing the null hypothesis that there is no relation between the row and column classifications in a two-way table.

C. Test the null hypothesis of "no relation" using the chi-square statistic and critical values from the chi-square distribution.

# SELF-TEST QUESTIONS

**24.1** In an experiment on what influences opinion, students were asked whether they agree or disagree with the following statement: " I hold that a little rebellion, now and then, is a good thing, and as necessary in the political world as storms are in the physical." One group was told that Thomas Jefferson said this, and a second group was told that Lenin said it. The data were (from Professor Thomas Moore of Grinnell College)

| | Agree | Disagree |
|---|---|---|
| Jefferson | 50 | 6 |
| Lenin | 42 | 14 |

We want to know whether there is good evidence that the source of the quotation influences whether students agree with it.
(a) Give a numerical description of the size of the effect we are looking for.
(b)Use a two-sample $z$ test to assess the significance of the effect. State the hypotheses, give the $P$-value, and report your conclusion.
(c) Use the chi-square test to answer the same question.

**24.2** In a study of the effect of parents' smoking habits on the smoking habits of high school students, researchers interviewed students in eight high schools in Arizona. The results appear in the following two-way table. (From S. V. Zagona, (ed.), *Studies and Issues in Smoking Behavior*, University of Arizona Press, Tucson, 1967, pages 157–180.)

| | Student smokes | Student does not smoke |
|---|---|---|
| Both parents smoke | 400 | 1380 |
| One parent smokes | 416 | 1823 |
| Neither parent smokes | 188 | 1168 |

(a) Describe the association between the smoking habits of parents and their high school children numerically. Summarize the results in plain language.
(b) How significant is the observed association?

## SELF-TEST SOLUTIONS

**24.1** The experiment compares two populations, students told the quotation is from Jefferson (Population 1) and those told it is from Lenin

(Population 2). We have a separate sample from each population. Here is the table with the sample sizes (row totals) added. These sample sizes were fixed in advance as part of the design of the study. The column and table totals are also given.

| | Agree | Disagree | Total |
|---|---|---|---|
| Jefferson | 50 | 6 | 56 |
| Lenin | 42 | 14 | 56 |
| Total | 92 | 20 | 112 |

(a) The sample proportions who agree are

$$\hat{p}_1 = \frac{50}{56} = 0.893$$
$$\hat{p}_2 = \frac{42}{56} = 0.750$$

This comparison (89% agree with Jefferson and 75% with Lenin) shows the size of the effect.
(b) To judge its significance, test the null hypothesis that the proportions who agree are the same in both populations:

$$H_0 : p_1 = p_2$$

$$H_a : p_1 \neq p_2$$

First calculate the pooled proportion who agree,

$$\hat{p} = \frac{50+42}{56+56} = \frac{92}{112} = 0.821$$

and then the $z$ statistic

$$s_p = \sqrt{\hat{p}(1-\hat{p})\left(\frac{1}{n_1} + \frac{1}{n_2}\right)}$$

$$
\begin{aligned}
&= \sqrt{(.821)(.179)\left(\frac{1}{56}+\frac{1}{56}\right)} = 0.0724 \\
z &= \frac{\hat{p}_1 - \hat{p}_2}{s_p} \\
&= \frac{.893 - .750}{.0724} = 1.98
\end{aligned}
$$

Because $z = 1.98$ lies between the 0.025 and 0.02 upper critical values in Table D, the $P$-value for the two-sided test lies between 0.05 and 0.04. The exact $P$-value is found from Table A as $2P(Z \geq 1.98) = 0.0478$. There is reasonably strong evidence of a difference between the two treatments.

(c) The chi-square test in this case tests exactly the same hypothesis, no difference between the two population proportions. To find the chi-square statistic, first calculate the expected cell counts by

$$\text{expected count} = \frac{\text{row total} \times \text{column total}}{n}$$

The result is

| | Agree | Disagree | Total |
|---|---|---|---|
| Jefferson | 46 | 10 | 56 |
| Lenin | 46 | 10 | 56 |
| Total | 92 | 20 | 112 |

The row and column totals are always the same for the observed and expected counts. The chi-square statistic is

$$
\begin{aligned}
X^2 &= \sum \frac{(\text{observed count} - \text{expected count})^2}{\text{expected count}} \\
&= \frac{(50-46)^2}{46} + \frac{(6-10)^2}{10} + \frac{(42-46)^2}{46} + \frac{(14-10)^2}{10} \\
&= 3.89
\end{aligned}
$$

The degrees of freedom are

$$(r-1)(c-1) = (2-1)(2-1) = 1$$

From Table G, we see that $X^2 = 3.89$ lies between the 0.05 and 0.025 critical values of the chi-square distribution with 1 degree of freedom. So the $P$-value of the test lies between these two values.

The two tests in (b) and (c) are in fact exactly equivalent. The chi-square statistic $X^2$ is exactly the square of the $z$ statistic (up to roundoff error). The $\chi^2(1)$ critical values are exactly the squares of the standard normal critical values, so the $P$-value is the same for both tests. When a two-way table is larger than $2 \times 2$, however, the $z$ test does not apply and you must use the chi-square test.

**24.2** In this case, a single sample of students is classified in two ways, by their parents' smoking behavior and their own smoking. Here is the $3 \times 2$ table with the totals included.

| | Student smokes | Student does not smoke | Total |
|---|---|---|---|
| Both parents smoke | 400 | 1380 | 1780 |
| One parent smokes | 416 | 1823 | 2239 |
| Neither parent smokes | 188 | 1168 | 1356 |
| Total | 1004 | 4371 | 5375 |

(a) The clearest way to describe the association is to compare the percent of students who smoke for each class of parents. When both parents smoke, the percent of students who smoke is

$$\frac{400}{1780} = 0.224 = 22.4\%$$

Similarly, the percent of smokers is 18.6% among students with one smoking parent and 13.9% when neither parent smokes. So students of

smokers are more likely to be smokers themselves.
(b) Because the sample is so large (5,375 students), we know that the observed association will be highly significant. The expected counts are

| | Student smokes | Student does not smoke | Total |
|---|---|---|---|
| Both parents smoke | 332.5 | 1447.5 | 1780 |
| One parent smokes | 418.2 | 1820.8 | 2239 |
| Neither parent smokes | 253.3 | 1102.7 | 1356 |
| Total | 1004 | 4371 | 5375 |

For example, the upper left expected count is

$$\frac{(1780)(1004)}{5375} = 332.5$$

Check your arithmetic by verifying that the row and column sums are the same for the expected counts as for the observed counts in the original table. The chi-square statistic is

$$\begin{aligned} X^2 &= \sum \frac{(\text{observed count} - \text{expected count})^2}{\text{expected count}} \\ &= \frac{(400 - 332.5)^2}{332.5} + \frac{(1380 - 1447.5)^2}{1447.5} + \cdots + \frac{(1168 - 1102.7)^2}{1102.7} \\ &= 37.57 \end{aligned}$$

The degrees of freedom are

$$(r-1)(c-1) = (3-1)(2-1) = (2)(1) = 2$$

Table G shows that the 0.0005 critical value for the $\chi^2(2)$ distribution is 15.20. The observed $X^2 = 37.57$ is far beyond 15.20, so the $P$-value is less than 0.0005. As expected, an observed association this large is extremely unlikely to occur by chance alone.

# UNIT 25
# INFERENCE FOR RELATIONSHIPS

## LESSON OVERVIEW

Association between two categorical variables is displayed in a two-way table, and the null hypothesis that no association is present is tested by the chi-square test discussed in Unit 24. Association between two quantitative variables is displayed by a scatterplot. If the association between an explanatory variable and a response variable is linear, it is described by a regression line. This unit discusses inference about linear relationships. You may want to review least-squares regression from Units 8 and 9 before studying this unit. Before using the inference methods in this unit, check that the data show a linear relationship and look for outliers and influential observations.

Confidence intervals and tests always make statements about parameters of the population from which our data are a sample. To this point, we have learned methods for inference about population means and population proportions. To talk about inference in the linear regression setting, we must first say what parameters we will draw conclusions about. The statistical model for **simple linear regression** says that in the population the mean of the response variable $y$ depends on the explanatory variable $x$ in a straight line fashion. The notation $\mu_y$ stands for "the mean of the response $y$" but we understand that this mean depends on the value of the explanatory variable $x$. The model for the population says first that

$$\mu_y = \beta_0 + \beta_1 x$$

The slope $\beta_1$ and intercept $\beta_0$ of this population regression line are unknown parameters that we want to draw conclusions about.

In the video, the first example concerns the expanding universe. There is a linear relation between the speed $y$ at which a galaxy is receding from us and its distance $x$. The slope $\beta_1$ is called the Hubble constant, and says how fast the universe is expanding. Astronomers very badly want an accurate estimate of $\beta_1$.

When we have $n$ observations on the variables $x$ and $y$, we estimate the unknown $\beta_1$ and $\beta_0$ by the slope $b_1$ and intercept $b_0$ of the **least-squares regression line.** That is, we let the least-squares line that we fit to the data estimate the unknown population regression line. To emphasize that the $b$'s estimate the $\beta$'s we use a different notation than in Unit 8: The least-squares line is now $\hat{y} = b_0 + b_1 x$.

Estimating $\beta_1$ and $\beta_0$ by $b_1$ and $b_0$ is much like using the sample mean $\overline{x}$ to estimate a population mean $\mu$. In both cases, we need information about the distribution of the population in order to move on to confidence intervals or tests of significance. The rest of the statistical model for regression says that the response $y_i$ to the value $x_i$ of the explanatory variable has a normal distribution, and that the standard deviation $\sigma$ of $y_i$ is the same for all values of $x$. The mean of $y_i$ does change with $x_i$: it is $\beta_0 + \beta_1 x_i$.

The standard deviation $\sigma$ describes how variable the response is. Variation is not measured around a fixed center but about the population regression line, because the mean of $y$ changes with $x$. To give a test or confidence interval, we must estimate $\sigma$. Recall the **residuals**

$$\begin{aligned} e_i &= \text{observed y} - \text{predicted y} \\ &= y_i - \hat{y}_i \end{aligned}$$

The sample variance of $y$ about the least-squares line is

$$s^2 = \frac{\sum e_i^2}{n-2}$$

The square root $s$ of this variance is our estimate of $\sigma$. The number $n-2$ is the **degrees of freedom** of $s$.

The preliminary calculations in a regression problem are: First, calculate the least-squares line $\hat{y} = b_0 + b_1 x$; and second, calculate the residuals from this line and the standard deviation $s$. These calculations are quite lengthy, so that you should use a statistical calculator or software whenever possible. In exercises, we will give you this basic information. You are *not* required to obtain $s$ by hand calculation.

Several kinds of inference are possible in the regression setting. This unit presents the two most important: **inference about the slope** $\beta_1$ of the population line, and **prediction** of the response for a given $x$. The Hubble constant story in the video illustrates inference about the slope. Using ultrasound data about the growth of a fetus to predict birth date, the other story in the video, is an example of predicting the response $y$ in regression. Both kinds of inference use $t$ procedures and the $t$ distribution with $n-2$ degrees of freedom. Although the formulas are more complicated, the ideas are similar to $t$ procedures for the mean $\mu$ of a population. The similarity is due to the fact that the estimated slope $b_1$ and the predicted response $\hat{y} = b_0 + b_1 x$ both have normal distributions. You can find detailed formulas in the text. All make use of the basic calculations of $b_1$, $b_0$, and $s$.

Because the slope $\beta_1$ is the change in $y$ (on the average) when $x$ increases by 1, it is the most important parameter that describes the relationship between $x$ and $y$. The level $C$ confidence interval for $\beta_1$ is

$$b_1 \pm t^* s_{b_1}$$

Throughout this unit $t^*$ is the upper $(1 - C)/2$ critical value of the $t(n - 2)$ distribution; $s_{b_1}$ is the standard error (estimated standard deviation) of the statistic $b_1$. To test the null hypothesis

$$H_0 : \beta_1 = 0$$

use the $t$ statistic

$$t = \frac{b_1}{s_{b_1}}$$

$H_0$ states that there is no linear relationship between $x$ and $y$, or that straight line dependence on $x$ is of no value in explaining $y$. Inference about the intercept $\beta_0$ is similar but is less often important.

To predict the **mean response** $\mu_y$ to a given value $x^*$ of the explanatory variable $x$, we use the value $\hat{\mu} = b_0 + b_1 x^*$ of the least-squares line when $x$ is $x^*$. The confidence interval for the mean response is

$$\hat{\mu} \pm t^* s_{\hat{\mu}}$$

Instead of predicting the mean (long-term average) response, we may wish to predict the **individual response** $y$ on a particular future occasion when $x$ has the value $x^*$. Again use the predicted value from the least-squares line, $\hat{y} = b_0 + b_1 x^*$. There is more variation in predicting a single future $y$ than in predicting the mean response $\mu_y$ on all occasions when $x^*$ is the value of $x$. So the **prediction interval** for $y$ is wider than the confidence interval for $\mu_y$. It has the form

$$\hat{y} \pm t^* s_{\hat{y}}$$

In these intervals, $\hat{\mu}$ and $\hat{y}$ are the same—the notation is just to remind us what we are using the least-squares line to predict. The standard error $s_{\hat{y}}$ is similar to $s_{\hat{\mu}}$, but has an extra term that reflects the additional variation in an individual observation.

## ASSIGNMENT

1. Read the LEARNING OBJECTIVES to see what specific skills you must acquire from this unit.

2. Read Section 9.1 of the text, omitting the subsection on "Inference for Correlation."

3. Do the following problems from the SECTION 9.1 EXERCISES in the text: 9.1, 9.2, 9.17.

4. Finally, try the SELF-TEST QUESTIONS and compare your answers with those given.

## LEARNING OBJECTIVES

A. Recognize what the simple linear regression model says about the relation between an explanatory variable $x$ and a response variable $y$, and explain the meaning of the parameters $\beta_1$, $\beta_0$, and $\sigma$ in this model.

B. Be able to use the least-squares regression line $\hat{y} = b_0 + b_1 x$ and the standard deviation about the line $s$ for inference in the regression setting, when these values are given by software.

C. Recognize when inference about the slope $\beta_1$ is called for. Use the $t$ procedures to carry out tests or confidence intervals for $\beta_1$.

D. Recognize when prediction is called for and the distinction between predicting a mean response and an individual response.

E. Use $t$ procedures to give a confidence interval for the mean response to a stated value of $x$ and to give a prediction interval for an individual future response.

## SELF-TEST QUESTIONS

A college gives a placement test to new students in order to place them into the proper mathematics course. Perhaps the mathematics part of the Scholastic Aptitude Tests (SAT-M) taken in high school can be used to predict how students will do on the placement test. Here are data on these two scores for 10 students.

| SAT-M | 700 | 512 | 412 | 572 | 484 | 624 | 684 | 692 | 612 | 462 |
|---|---|---|---|---|---|---|---|---|---|---|
| Placement | 94 | 76 | 52 | 65 | 71 | 92 | 87 | 83 | 79 | 61 |

A computer regression routine gives the least-squares regression line of the placement score $y$ on the SAT-M score $x$ as

$$\hat{y} = 8.914 + 0.11659x$$

and the variance $s^2$ of the $y$'s about the line (called MSE in the computer output) as

$$s^2 = 49.1780$$

The problems below refer to this situation.

**25.1** (a) Plot the data and draw the regression line on your plot. Are there any clear outliers or influential observations that cause you to doubt the usefulness of the least-squares line?
(b) How much do placement scores increase (on the average) for every point increase in the SAT-M score?
(c) Is the straight line relationship between $x$ and $y$ that appears on your plot statistically significant? (Give a $P$-value.)

**25.2** (a) Give a 90% confidence interval for the mean placement test score of all students who score 600 on the SAT-M.
(b) Julie Jones scores 600 on the SAT-M. Would a 90% prediction interval for Julie's placement score be wider or narrower than your interval in (a)? Would it have the same center or a different center?
(c) The college would like to predict placement scores more precisely. That is, it would like narrower intervals without sacrificing confidence. What do you recommend?

## SELF-TEST SOLUTIONS

**25.1** (a) The plot appears in Figure 25.1. (An easy way to draw the line is to find $\hat{y}$ for two values of $x$ and draw the line through these two points.) There is a moderately strong straight line relationship with no outliers or influential observations.

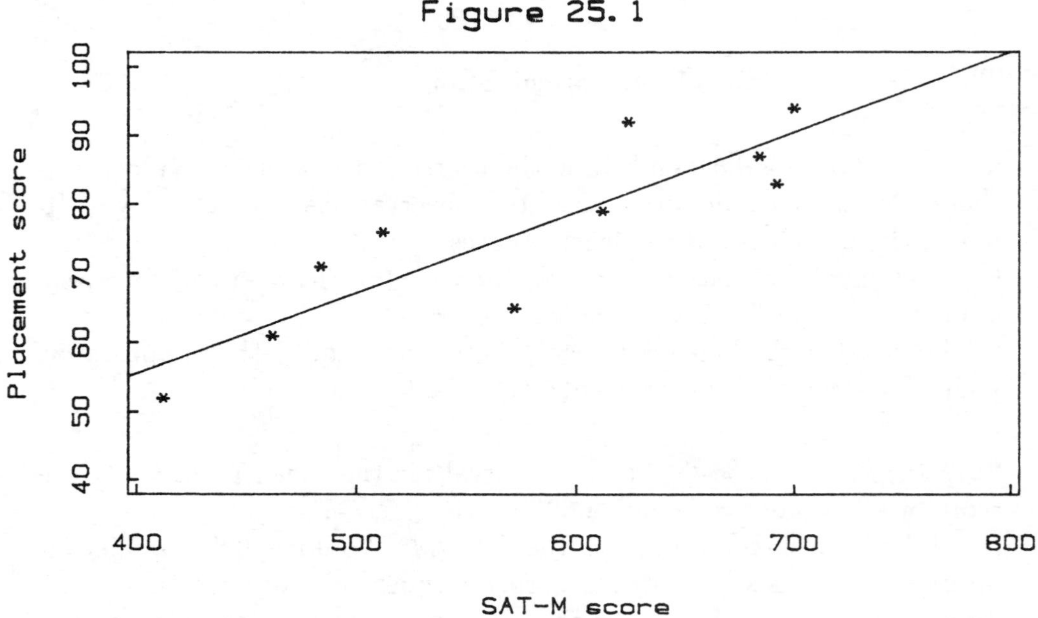


(b) This is the slope $\beta_1$ of the true regression line, and is estimated by the slope of the fitted line, $b_1 = 0.11659$. The placement score increases by about one-tenth of a point for every point increase in the SAT-M.
(c) This calls for a test of the hypothesis

$$H_0 : \beta_1 = 0$$

that there is no relationship against the two-sided alternative

$$H_a : \beta_1 \neq 0$$

To calculate the test statistic, first find from the SAT-M data that

$$\sum(x - \overline{x})^2 = 96,560.4$$

If your calculator computes the variance from keyed-in data, it is quicker to find the variance $s_x^2$ of the $x$ values and use the fact that

$$\sum(x-\bar{x})^2 = (n-1)s_x^2$$

The standard error of the estimated slope $b_1$ is

$$\begin{aligned} s_{b_1} &= \frac{s}{\sqrt{\sum(x-\bar{x})^2}} \\ &= \frac{\sqrt{49.1780}}{\sqrt{96,560.4}} \\ &= \frac{7.0127}{310.7417} = 0.02257 \end{aligned}$$

Finally, the $t$ statistic is

$$\begin{aligned} t &= \frac{b_1}{s_{b_1}} \\ &= \frac{0.11659}{0.02257} = 5.166 \end{aligned}$$

Compare $t = 5.166$ to the critical values of the $t$ distribution with degrees of freedom

$$n-2 = 10-2 = 8$$

in Table E. The 0.0005 critical value is 5.041, and $t$ lies above this value. So the $P$-value for the two-sided test is smaller than 0.001 (remember to double the table value for a two-sided test). The linear relationship shown in the scatterplot is highly significant.

**25.2** The predicted mean placement score is found from the regression line by substituting the specified value $x^* = 600$

$$\begin{aligned} \hat{\mu} &= b_0 + b_1 x \\ &= 8.914 + (0.11659)(600) = 78.87 \end{aligned}$$

This prediction is the center of the confidence interval. The margin of error depends on the standard error of the prediction, which is

$$\begin{aligned} s_{\hat{\mu}} &= s\sqrt{\frac{1}{n}+\frac{(x^*-\overline{x})^2}{\sum(x-\overline{x})^2}} \\ &= 7.0127\sqrt{\frac{1}{10}+\frac{(600-575.4)^2}{96,560.4}} \\ &= 7.0127\sqrt{0.10627} = 2.286 \end{aligned}$$

The confidence interval uses the critical value of the $t(8)$ distribution for $C = 90\%$, which Table E gives as $t^* = 1.860$. The interval is

$$\begin{aligned} \hat{\mu} \pm t^* s_{\hat{\mu}} &= 78.87 \pm (1.860)(2.286) \\ &= 78.87 \pm 4.25 \\ &= (74.62,\quad 83.12) \end{aligned}$$

(b) The prediction interval for the placement score of an individual whose SAT-M score is $x^* = 600$ has the same center as the confidence interval for the mean placement score of all students who score 600 on the SAT-M. In both cases, the prediction is given by the regression line. But the prediction interval for an individual score is wider than the confidence interval for the mean score, because individual scores vary about the mean. This added variation appears as an added term in the standard error and results in a wider interval.

(c) These intervals are based on data from only 10 students. The linear relationship is strong enough to be promising. The college should use data from more students, preferably several hundred, to obtain narrower intervals.

# UNIT 26
# CASE STUDY: DEVELOPING AZT

## LESSON OVERVIEW

The final video program of *Against All Odds: Inside Statistics* presents a case study that illustrates the full range of statistical ideas that we have met. New pharmaceutical products are required by federal law and regulation to present statistical evidence that they are safe and effective. The case study looks at the development of one such product, AZT, the first drug shown to be effective in prolonging the life of AIDS patients. Randomized comparative experiments were conducted first on animals, then with a few human subjects to determine safety, dosage and possible side effects, then with many human subjects to establish effectiveness. This last clinical trial was double-blind and (because no other treatment for AIDS was known) compared AZT to a placebo. It found statistically significant evidence that AZT is more effective than a placebo. After AZT was approved for use, follow-up studies continued to collect data from users.

The purpose of this unit is not to introduce new material, but to reinforce the ways of thinking statistically that you have learned during the series. The sample examination that concludes the unit emphasizes inference, but uses material from earlier portions of the course as needed.

## ASSIGNMENT

1. Review the previously assigned sections of Chapters 6 to 9 of the text and your corrected assignments and self-tests on Units 19 to 25.

2. Do the following problems from the CHAPTER EXERCISES at the end of Chapters 6 to 8 in the text: 6.65, 6.69, 6.73, 7.73, 7.81, 8.49, 8.55, and 9.23 from the SECTION 9.1 EXERCISES.

3. Work SAMPLE EXAMINATION 3 under examination conditions (that is, without referring to the text unless examinations in your course are open-book). Compare your answers with the solutions given, and review again any material that you had trouble with.

# SAMPLE EXAMINATION 3

## PART I–MULTIPLE CHOICE–2 POINTS EACH

**1** An opinion poll asks a random sample of adults whether they favor banning ownership of handguns by private citizens. A commentator believes that more than half of all adults favor such a ban. To assess this claim, you would test
(a) $H_0 : \mu = 0$ against $H_a : \mu > 0$
(b) $H_0 : p = 1/2$ against $H_a : p > 1/2$
(c) $H_0 : p = 1/2$ against $H_a : p \neq 1/2$
(d) $H_0 : p > 1/2$ against $H_a : p = 1/2$

**2** You read that Scholastic Aptitude Test scores in high school explain only 9% of the variation in students' later grades in college. The correlation between SAT scores and college grades is therefore
(a) $r = 0.9$
(b) $r = 0.81$
(c) $r = 0.09$
(d) $r = 0.3$
(e) $r = 0.03$

Questions 3 to 6 refer to the following situation. A study compares two methods of teaching reading. The study is carried out in a large elementary school. Third graders in this school are divided at random into two groups. One group is taught by Method A, the other by Method B. At the end of the school year, all of the children are given a standard test of reading ability.

**3** The response variable in this study is
(a) the reading test scores
(b) the teaching methods
(c) the third graders
(d) the schools

**4** The design of the study is
(a) a completely randomized experiment
(b) a randomized block experiment
(c) a simple random sample
(d) a stratified random sample

**5** To see if the study gives evidence of a difference in the effectiveness of the two teaching methods, you would test hypotheses of the form
(a) $H_0 : \mu_1 = \mu_2$ against $H_0 : \mu_1 > \mu_2$
(b) $H_0 : \mu = 0$ against $H_a : \mu > 0$
(c) $H_0 : \mu_1 = \mu_2$ against $H_a : \mu_1 \neq \mu_2$
(d) $H_0 : \mu = 0$ against $H_a : \mu \neq 0$

**6** Of the tests of significance you have learned, the most appropriate for analyzing the results of this study is the
(a) two-sample $t$ test
(b) matched pairs $t$ test
(c) single-sample $t$ test
(d) two-sample $z$ test for proportions

Questions 7 to 10 are based on the following situation. A news report says that a national opinion poll of 1500 randomly selected adults found that 43% thought they would be worse off during the next year. The news report went on to say that the margin of error in the poll result is ±3 percentage points with 95% confidence.

**7** This margin of error does *not* include errors due to
(a) the fact that the poll dialed telephone numbers at random and so missed all people without phones
(b) the fact that the poll could not contact some people whose numbers were chosen
(c) chance variation in the random selection
(d) both (a) and (b)
(e) all of (a), (b), and (c)

**8** A 90% confidence interval based on the poll results would have a margin of error
(a) less than $\pm 3$ percentage points
(b) equal to $\pm 3$ percentage points
(c) greater than $\pm 3$ percentage points
(d) any of the above—the margin of error is random

**9** If the poll had interviewed 1000 persons rather than 1500 (and still found 43% believing they would be worse off), the margin of error for 95% confidence would be
(a) less than $\pm 3$ percentage points
(b) equal to $\pm 3$ percentage points
(c) greater than $\pm 3$ percentage points
(d) any of the above—the margin of error is random

**10** If the poll had obtained the outcome 43% by a similar random sampling method from all adults in New York State (population 18 million) instead of from all adults in the U.S. (population 249 million), the margin of error for 95% confidence would be
(a) less than $\pm 3$ percentage points
(b) equal to $\pm 3$ percentage points
(c) greater than $\pm 3$ percentage points

(d) any of the above—the margin of error is random

**11** The ARSMA test is a psychological test that measures the degree to which Mexican Americans have adapted to Anglo culture. ARSMA scores in the population of Mexican Americans are normally distributed with mean 3.0 and standard deviation 0.8. Fernando scores 1.8 on the test. What is his standardized score?
(a) $z = -1.95$
(b) $z = -1.2$
(c) $z = 1.5$
(d) $z = -1.5$

**12** What percent of all Mexican Americans have ARSMA scores higher than Fernando's 1.8 (see the previous question)?
(a) 3.59%
(b) 93.32%
(c) 88.49%
(d) 6.68%
(e) 97.44%

**13** A study of the distribution of blood types measures the blood type (A, B, AB, or O) of almost 10,000 people. The study includes people living in Florida, Minnesota, and California. The chi-square test is used to see if there are differences among the distributions of blood types in the three locations. The degrees of freedom for this test are
(a) 9,999
(b) 6
(c) 12
(d) 2

**14** In a test of the anti-fungus activity of a chemical compound, fungus

is grown in petri dishes with different concentrations of the compound and the diameter of the fungus colonies is measured after one day. There are 20 dishes, two at each of 10 concentrations. A plot of diameter against concentration shows a straight line pattern, with higher concentrations giving smaller diameters. Least squares regression is used to analyze the data. What distribution is used in the test of the hypothesis that concentration has no effect on diameter?
(a) $t(18)$
(b) $t(19)$
(c) $t(9)$
(d) $t(8)$

**15** Michael wants to estimate the mean time the college computer system will take to run a program and return the output. He submits the program at 8 times, randomly chosen during a 24-hour period. Because the run times are much longer at peak use periods, the distributions of the results is strongly skewed to the right. What procedure should Michael use to give a confidence interval for the mean run time during the entire day?
(a) A one-sample $t$ procedure
(b) Least squares regression and prediction
(c) The chi-square procedure for two-way tables
(d) None of these should be used

**16** The number $t^*$ with probability 0.20 falling below it in the $t$ distribution with 5 degrees of freedom is
(a) 2.757
(b) 0.920
(c) $-0.920$
(d) $-2.757$

**17** A significance test based on your data allows you to reject a hypothesis $H_0$ in favor of an alternative $H_a$ at the 5% level of significance. What can you say about significance at the 1% level?
(a) The test can never be significant at the 1% level
(b) The test may or may not be significant at the 1% level
(c) The test will always be significant at the 1% level
(d) The test will be significant if one-sided but not if two-sided

**18** Albinism (absence of pigment in skin, hair, and eyes) is hereditary. If two carriers of the albinism gene marry, each child has probability 1/4 of being albino, independent of other children. The probability that all of the three children of such a couple are albino is
(a) 0.4219
(b) 0.0156
(c) 0.75
(d) 0.25

**19** There is an approximately linear relationship between household income and the percent of income that is saved (prosperous households save a higher percentage of their income). An economist has data on income and savings last year for a sample of households. She fits a least squares line and gives a 95% confidence interval for the mean percent of income saved by all households with $50,000 annual income. The Cuellar family earned $50,000. The 95% interval used to predict the percent of their income that the Cuellars save is
(a) wider than the 95% interval for all households
(b) the same as the 95% interval for all households
(c) the same width as the 95% interval for all households, but with a different center
(d) narrower than the 95% interval for all households

**20** An industrial experiment compares the degree of microporosity (which eventually leads to cracks and failure in use) in aluminum alloy produced under two conditions. Ultrasound measurements on 5 ingots produced by the first method give $\overline{x}_1 = 4.4$ and $s_1 = 0.8$. Similar measurements on 6 ingots produced by the second method have $\overline{x}_2 = 3.8$ and $s_2 = 1.0$. The standard error of the difference in means $\overline{x}_2 - \overline{x}_1$ is
(a) 0.766
(b) 0.543
(c) 0.197
(d) 0.295

# PART II

**1** (15 points) The Family Adaptability and Cohesion Evaluation Scales (FACES) is a psychological test that measures two different aspects of family behavior. One of these is "cohesion," which is the degree to which family members are emotionally connected to each other. The test is given to individuals, who may give their family a different cohesion score than would other family members. A researcher administers FACES to a sample of 33 adults in families with a runaway teenager. The mean cohesion score is $\overline{x} = 36.9$ and the standard deviation is $s = 4.9$.
(a) Give a 95% confidence interval for the mean cohesion (as rated by an adult) of families with runaway teenagers.
(b) The FACES cohesion scores for all adults have mean 40. The researcher believes that families of runaways have lower cohesion than do other families. Does the sample give good evidence for this belief? State hypotheses, give a $P$-value, and report your conclusion.
(c) What assumptions are required by the procedures you used in (a) and (b)? Which of these assumptions is most important if the

researcher is to draw conclusions about all families with runaway teenagers?

**2** (10 points) The late 1970's saw two very severe winters that greatly decreased the population of upland game birds in the midwest. In 1978, a wildlife biologist made walkthrough counts of pheasants on 8 plots of land in northern Indiana where counts of pheasants had been made by the same method in 1976. The counts, in birds per 10 acres, were:

| Plot | A | B | C | D | E | F | G | H |
|---|---|---|---|---|---|---|---|---|
| 1976 Count | 6.9 | 0.1 | 13.5 | 6.6 | 4.2 | 9.0 | 10.5 | 1.4 |
| 1978 Count | 2.6 | 0.0 | 10.3 | 0.7 | 0.0 | 3.0 | 6.2 | 0.0 |

Give a 90% confidence interval for the reduction in pheasant population density (birds per 10 acres of land) in Northern Indiana.

**3** (18 points) A landmark in understanding the universe is Hubble's discovery of a linear relationship between the distance $x$ of other galaxies and the velocity $y$ at which they are moving away from us. Hubble used 24 galaxies whose distance could be measured with reasonable accuracy. Figure 26.1 is a scatterplot of his data with the least squares regression line. ( Data from Edwin P. Hubble, "A relation between distance and radial velocity among extra-galactic nebulae," *Proceedings of the National Academy of Sciences*, 15(1929), pages 168–173.)

Statistical software gives the following information. (The "residual standard error" is $s$, the estimated standard deviation about the fitted line.)

```
           Coefficient  Standard Error          t
Intercept       87.095        69.56830    1.25193
Distance      371.9073        62.72996    5.92870
```

```
Residual standard error = 194.1925   r-squared = 0.6150
```

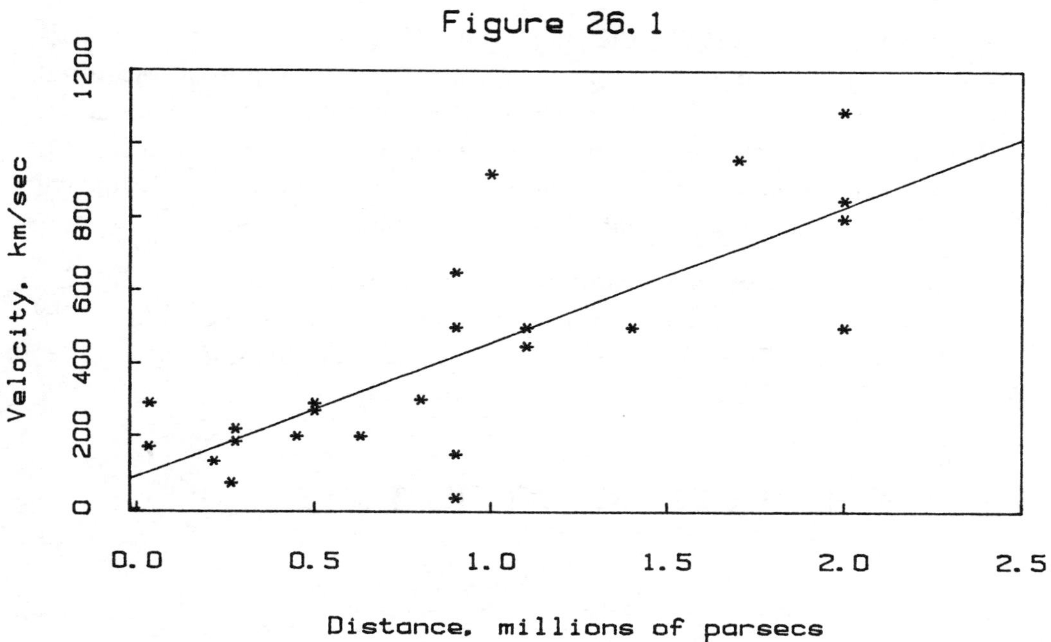


(a) The scatterplot shows considerable scatter about the line, due to the difficulty of measuring both distance and velocity. Are there any influential observations that lead you to mistrust the least squares fit?
(b) How much does the velocity of a galaxy increase on the average when the distance increases by one unit? (The unit of distance is $10^6$ parsecs.) Give a 90% confidence interval as your answer. This number is important for describing the expanding universe.
(c) How fast do you predict that a galaxy $10^6$ parsecs distant is moving away from us? Give a 90% confidence interval for the mean velocity

of all galaxies at that distance. (At your request, the computer tells you that Hubble's 24 distances have mean $\overline{x} = 0.9114$ and variance $s_x^2 = 0.4167$.)

**4** (17 points) In a study of the effect of political party affiliation on attitudes toward affirmative action programs, random samples of registered Democratic and Republican voters in a western city were selected. Of the 200 Democrats, 122 favored affirmative action, 63 opposed it, and 15 had no opinion. Among the 200 Republicans, 109 favored affirmative action, 70 were opposed, and 21 had no opinion.

Describe the differences in opinion between Democrats and Republicans and give numbers to back your description. Are the observed differences statistically significant? Give a $P$-value to answer this question.

# SAMPLE EXAMINATION 3 SOLUTIONS

## PART I ANSWERS

**1** (b) The hypotheses concern the proportion $p$ of adults who favor banning handguns. The commentator's claim is $H_a$, the effect being sought, while $H_0$ is "no effect."

**2** (d) The proportion of variance explained is $r^2$.

**3** (a)

**4** (a) All of the subjects (students) are assigned at random to the experimental treatments (teaching methods).

**5** (c) The $\mu$'s are the mean reading scores for the two methods. No direction for $H_a$ is specified.

**6** (a)

**7** (d) The margin of error in confidence intervals includes *only* random sampling error. Undercoverage of the population, as in (a), and nonresponse, as in (b), are not included.

**8** (a) Lower confidence produces a narrower interval from the same data.

**9** (c) Fewer observations produce a wider margin of error.

**10** (b) The margin of error depends on the size of the sample, but not on the size of the population when the population is much larger than the sample.

**11** (d) The standardized score is $z = (x - \mu)/\sigma = (1.8 - 3)/0.8$.

**12** (b) The entry in Table A for $z = -1.5$ is 0.0668, so the proportion with *higher* scores is 0.9332.

**13** (b) This is a $4 \times 3$ table, so the degrees of freedom are $(r-1)(c-1) = 3 \times 2$.

**14** (a) There are $n = 20$ data points, and the degrees of freedom for $t$ statistics in simple linear regression are $n - 2$.

**15** (d) Michael has a small sample ($n = 8$) from a strongly skewed distribution, so he cannot use the $t$ procedure that would be appropriate if the data were normally distributed.

**16** (c) Table E gives 0.920 as the point with probability 0.20 above it. Because the $t$ distributions are symmetric about 0, there is also probability 0.20 below $-0.920$.

**17** (b) The test statistic is in the extreme 5% of its distribution; it may be in the extreme 1%, but need not be.

**18** (b) You can use Table C of binomial probabilities, with $n = 3$ and $p = 0.25$, or use the multiplication rule for independent events: $.25 \times .25 \times .25$.

**19** (a) The prediction interval for a single response has the same center as the confidence interval for the mean of all responses, but is wider.

**20** (b) The standard error (estimated standard deviation) is

$$\sqrt{\frac{s_1^2}{n_1} + \frac{s_2^2}{n_2}}$$

## PART II ANSWERS

**1** Both (a) and (b) involve inference about the mean cohesion score $\mu$ of the population of all families with a runaway teenager. The one-sample $t$ procedures are appropriate. Because the sample size is $n = 33$, the $t(32)$ distribution is used. Table E does not have entries for 32 degrees of freedom, so we use the next smaller available degrees of freedom, 30.

(a) The 95% confidence interval requires the critical value of $t(30)$ for $C = 95\%$, which is $t^* = 2.042$. The interval is

$$\begin{aligned} \overline{x} \pm t^* \frac{s}{\sqrt{n}} &= 36.9 \pm 2.042 \frac{4.9}{\sqrt{33}} \\ &= 36.9 \pm 1.74 \\ &= (35.16, \ \ 38.64) \end{aligned}$$

(b) Because the researcher believes that this population has a mean lower than the overall mean 40, the alternative is one-sided:

$$H_0 : \mu = 40$$

$$H_a : \mu < 40$$

The one-sample $t$ statistic is

$$\begin{aligned} t &= \frac{\overline{x} - 40}{s/\sqrt{n}} \\ &= \frac{36.9 - 40}{4.9/\sqrt{33}} = -3.63 \end{aligned}$$

The $P$-value is the probability below $t = -3.63$ in the $t(30)$ distribution. By the symmetry of the $t$ distributions, this is the same as the probability above $t = 3.63$. Table E shows that 3.63 lies between the 0.001 and 0.0005 critical values of the $t(30)$ distribution. So $P$ is between 0.001 and 0.0005. This is very strong evidence that the population mean is less than 40.

(c) The $t$ procedures require (1) that the observations be an SRS from the population, and (2) that the population distribution be normal. When the sample is moderately large (greater than 15 as a rule of thumb), normality is not essential as long as outliers and strong skewness are not present. The SRS assumption is more important. If the sample is not typical of the population of families with runaway teenagers (perhaps they are all rich enough to seek family counseling, for example), the conclusions cannot be generalized to the entire population.

**2** This is a matched pairs study because the same 8 plots were surveyed in both years. The differences (1976 minus 1978) are

4.3 0.1 3.2 5.9 4.2 6.0 4.3 1.4

A normal quantile plot shows that these differences are approximately normal, so a $t$ confidence interval is justified.

Calculation shows that the mean and standard deviation of the 8 differences are

$$\overline{x} = 3.675 \qquad s = 2.056$$

The confidence interval uses the critical value $t^* = 1.895$ for $C = 90\%$ from the $t(7)$ distribution, found in Table E. (The $t(7)$ distribution applies because there are 8 observations.) The interval is

$$\begin{aligned} \overline{x} \pm t^* \frac{s}{\sqrt{n}} &= 3.675 \pm 1.895 \frac{2.056}{\sqrt{8}} \\ &= 3.675 \pm 1.377 \\ &= (2.30,\ \ 5.05) \end{aligned}$$

**3** (a) There are no influential observations, and no outliers more extreme than the general scatter of the data suggest. The $r^2$ of 61.5% shows a moderately strong linear relationship. We can use the least squares regression line.
(b) We want to estimate the slope $\beta_1$. The computer output tells us that

$$b_1 = 371.9073 \text{ and } s_{b_1} = 62.72996$$

Because $n = 24$ the degrees of freedom are $n - 2 = 22$. The 90% confidence interval uses the critical value $t^* = 1.717$ of the $t(22)$ distribution. The confidence interval is

$$\begin{aligned} b_1 \pm t^* s_{b_1} &= 371.9073 \pm (1.717)(62.72996) \\ &= 371.907 \pm 107.707 \\ &= (264.2, \quad 479.6) \end{aligned}$$

The width of the interval reflects the scatter of the data.
(c) To predict the velocity $y$ when $x = 1$, use the fitted line.

$$\begin{aligned} \hat{y} = 87.095 + 371.9073x &= 87.095 + (371.9073)(1) \\ &= 459.0023 \end{aligned}$$

This value is also $\hat{\mu}$, the predicted value of the mean velocity of all galaxies at this distance. For the confidence interval at $x^* = 1$ we first calculate

$$\begin{aligned} (x^* - \overline{x})^2 &= (1 - .9114)^2 = 0.007850 \\ \sum(x - \overline{x})^2 &= (n-1)s_x^2 = (23)(.4167) = 9.5841 \\ s_{\hat{\mu}} &= s\sqrt{\frac{1}{n} + \frac{(x^* - \overline{x})^2}{\sum(x - \overline{x})^2}} \\ &= 194.1925\sqrt{\frac{1}{24} + \frac{0.00785}{9.5841}} = 40.027 \end{aligned}$$

The confidence interval is

$$\begin{aligned} \hat{\mu} \pm t^* s_{\hat{\mu}} &= 459.0023 \pm (1.717)(40.027) \\ &= 459.0023 \pm 68.726 \\ &= (390.3, \quad 527.7) \end{aligned}$$

**4** The data are most clearly presented in a $2 \times 3$ table. The row totals are the sample sizes that were fixed in advance, while the column totals are random.

| | Favor | Oppose | No opinion | Total |
|---|---|---|---|---|
| Democrats | 122 | 63 | 15 | 200 |
| Republicans | 109 | 70 | 21 | 200 |
| Total | 231 | 133 | 36 | 400 |

To describe the differences, compare the percents of Democrats and Republicans who hold each opinion. In particular, 61% of Democrats favor affirmative action programs, while 54.5% of Republicans approve. The Republicans in the sample are somewhat less supportive than the Democrats, but a majority of both parties support affirmative action.

The significance of the differences between the Republican and Democratic distributions of responses is assessed by a chi-square test. The expected counts are:

| | Favor | Oppose | No opinion | Total |
|---|---|---|---|---|
| Democrats | 115.5 | 66.5 | 18 | 200 |
| Republicans | 115.5 | 66.5 | 18 | 200 |
| Total | 231 | 133 | 36 | 400 |

Notice that because the two samples are the same size, the expected counts are the same in both rows. The chi-square statistic is:

$$\begin{aligned} X^2 = &= \sum \frac{(\text{observed count} - \text{expected count})^2}{\text{expected count}} \\ &= \frac{(122-115.5)^2}{115.5} + \frac{(63-66.5)^2}{66.5} + \cdots + \frac{(21-18)^2}{18} \\ &= 2.100 \end{aligned}$$

Compare this value with critical values of the $\chi^2$ distribution with $(r-1)(c-1) = (1)(2) = 2$ degrees of freedom from Table G. The observed value 2.1 is less than the 0.25 critical value. So the observed differences between Democrats and Republicans could easily occur by chance if both parties had the same distribution of opinion. The observed differences between the samples are not statistically significant ($P > 0.25$).